CW00376549

The Vegetable Finder

*Sources for nearly 3000
commercially available
vegetable varieties*

New edition, revised and expanded

Published by the Henry Doubleday Research Association
Researching, demonstrating and promoting environmentally friendly
growing techniques

Edited by Jeremy Cherfas

Thanks to Patricia Carry, Simon Hickmott, Rachel Pearcey, Mike Penny and Michelle Rudge.

Cover artwork by Pete Lawrence.

Published by the Henry Doubleday Research Association
Ryton-on-Dunsmore, Coventry, CV8 3LG

Distributed by Moorland Publishing Co. Ltd
Moor Farm Road, Airfield Estate, Ashbourne, Derbyshire, DE6 1HD

© The Henry Doubleday Research Association 1994

ISBN 0-905343-19-0

Printed in Great Britain by The Cromwell Press Ltd
Broughton Gifford, Melksham, Wiltshire, SN12 8PH

Printed on environmentally friendly, acid-free paper from managed forests

All Rights Reserved. No part of this publication may be reproduced, stored in a retrieval system or transmitted in any form including photocopying without the written permission of the publisher.

Contents

Contents

Contents

Contents

Introduction

This new edition of The Vegetable Finder is considerably bigger, although it lists only a few more varieties, 2891 this year as against 2812 last. The increase is accounted for by our continuing policy of adding descriptions taken from the suppliers' catalogues. Where a variety still does not have a description it is either because the suppliers do not offer one or because we still have not had time to enter all of the information.

We have concentrated on providing descriptions for the open pollinated varieties because we believe that these varieties are most in need of protection, as a look at the Supplier Analysis (page 13) makes clear. Naturally, we would prefer people to favour open pollinated varieties. In future years, we may start to incorporate descriptions of hybrids, especially for vegetables such as sweetcorn where the overwhelming number of varieties available are in fact hybrids. Another plan is to add suppliers of fruit. Many of these are already listed in The Plant Finder, but it would probably make more sense to have them here, with useful descriptions, than to leave them there as bare names.

Using The Vegetable Finder is simple. For every commercially available variety there is an entry that indicates whether it is an F1 hybrid and gives a list of suppliers. To find details of the suppliers, match the codes with the entries at the back of the book. And if you want to preserve varieties, bear in mind that open-pollinated varieties with few suppliers are the ones most likely to need help.

There has been a slight decrease in the number of varieties available from just one supplier, 994 out of 2000 (49.7%) this year as against 1048 out of 1990 (52.7%) last year. It is far too early to say whether this represents a broadening of the base of supply or the dropping of varieties that were already on their last legs, economically speaking. One that we are particularly sad to find is missing is Russian Red kale; last year, Cottagers kale was dropped from the National List (though some suppliers are still offering it). Russian Red is still on the list, but nobody is offering it.

A word about some of the new, approved names for old varieties. Many familiar old varieties, such as Detroit beetroot, have sprouted a whole series of numbers. These numbers have been assigned after tests conducted at the request of the European Commission, to further harmonise the naming of varieties throughout the European Union. The details are complex, but essentially there is a change-over period, when a variety may be known by either its old name or its new name and number. If a variety has a number, then all catalogues are supposed to be using that number. Some aren't, yet, but all will in the end have to comply.

We compile and publish The Vegetable Finder first and foremost as a tool for gardeners, to enable them to find the varieties that suit them. Although the Heritage Seed Programme of the Henry Doubleday Research Association maintains a Seed Library of more than 500 varieties that are commercially extinct, we would far prefer to see varieties re-

main on sale, rather than relegated to the shelves of our fridges, which seems to be equivalent to saying that they are not worth growing. The reverse is true, of course; the older
varieties are often more suitable for the amateur and small-scale grower, but they are less
rewarding for the seed companies.

We continue to campaign for a change in the law, which currently treats all varieties
equally, whether they command commercial sales of hundreds of kilograms or amateur
sales of just a few hundred packets. It is absurd to fail to distinguish these two very different markets, a point of view that the Ministry of Agriculture, Fisheries and Food seems
belatedly to be coming round to. Quite what the new system will be, if it is ever enacted,
remains to be seen. The HDRA has offered its own suggestion for a scheme that combines
maximal protection for growers, breeders and seed suppliers with minimal operational
costs, and we remain hopeful. In the meantime, we can use The Vegetable Finder not only
to ease supply but also to analyse objectively the market.

Take potatoes. According to official figures from the Potato Marketing Board, three
varieties (Maris Bard, Pentland Javelin and Rocket) account for 62% of the area planted
to first early potatoes. For second earlies, the top three varieties (Estima, Wilja and Marfona)
occupy 72% of the crop. And for maincrops, the top three (Maris Piper, Record and Cara)
make up just under half – 49%–of the crop. These varieties are thus inevitably going to be
the easiest to buy in the shops. What of the gardener who wants to grow something different? Using The Vegetable Finder, we have discovered that the varieties that are easiest to
buy in the shops are also easiest to find as seed potatoes. There are 150 potato varieties
listed, but only 31 are available from 5 or more suppliers. Those 31 include the top three
commercial varieties in each maturity group. In other words, the varieties that are easiest
to buy for eating, in the shops, are also among the easiest to find as seed potatoes.

This coincidence does not reflect what gardeners want, at least not as far as anecdotal
evidence is concerned (and the HDRA is conducting a survey to get a truly representative
idea of what gardeners do want). It reflects the sad fact that gardeners are, by and large,
allowed to grow the left-overs of the commercial potato industry, a state of affairs that is
likely to persist unless there is a restructuring of the seed potato supply system.

At the other end of the scale, of the 150 available potato varieties, 81 are offered by a
single supplier, another 18 by two suppliers. At least one specialist potato supplier has
vanished since the previous edition of The Vegetable Finder and another definitely tee-
tered. If another potato specialist does vanish, so would many of the interesting, unusual
and rewarding varieties available to the amateur who is diligent enough to seek them out.

That would be bad enough, to deplete still further the legacy of old potato varieties, but
the problem is actually much more important than the question of consumer choice. It
concerns the security of our food supply. That just three varieties should so dominate the
plantings of first earlies, second earlies and maincrops is bad enough, because the lack of
genetic diversity in our potatoes (as in any crop) is an invitation to epidemics of disease.
The root cause of the Irish Potato Famine, a byword for the dangers of insufficient genetic
diversity, was the fact that all the potatoes being grown throughout Europe in the 1840s

were descended from just two varieties from the Andes, both of which were susceptible to late blight. Late blight came originally from Mexico, so it is not surprising that Andean potatoes had no resistance to it. Growers today may feel that they have the disease under control, and thanks to neater farming methods and chemical fungicides they probably do.

But there is no room for complacency. Since the 1840s, all the outbreaks of blight have been the work of just one strain of the fungus, called A1. More recently, another strain – A2 – has escaped from Mexico. For the first time in more than 150 years, blight outside Mexico will be able to enjoy sex, with all the opportunities for shuffling the genetic pack that such reproduction entails. Already, the A2 strain has appeared in the United States alongside resistance to metalaxyl, one of the fungicides that could always be counted on to control blight. As one report commented, "in North America, this is a nuisance. In countries such as India (which has tripled its potato production of the past 25 years), China (the world's leading potato producer) and much of Africa, it is a serious threat to the local food supply".

Fungicide resistance is just one trick that the new, sexually active blight could master. At present, blight cannot survive long outside the potato; sexually-produced spores might be able to live for years in the soil, rendering large areas unfit for potatoes. There could be greater virulence, faster spread, more damage. Nobody can predict how blight will develop, only that change is inevitable.

Our reliance on just a few varieties makes us especially vulnerable to whatever blight may throw at us. In Mexico, where farmers have lived for centuries with blight, their strategy depends on the use of as many varieties as possible. Whatever happens, they are sure of something to harvest. While potato breeders are busy plundering the old Mexican varieties and wild species for genes that may help in the rest of the world, we gardeners need access to as many varieties as possible. In past epidemics, such as the outbreak of Wart Disease that devastated crops in 1910, it was sharp-eyed inspectors who noticed that one variety, Golden Wonder, was apparently immune, and from that observation, and that variety, come most of the immune varieties available today. The more varieties are out there growing, in as many places as possible, the more likely we are to discover valuable traits such as resistance. It is no good simply having the potatoes locked up in government or private collections; they need to be out there, growing and exposed to all the challenges going, to make their qualities visible. Unfortunately, with the structure of the seed potato supply system so rigged towards commercial growers, it seems unlikely that things will get any better before they get much worse.

As with true seeds, ordinary gardeners can make a difference. Seek out the more unusual potato varieties and you will help to establish the demand for them. With luck, and responsive suppliers, availability will increase in future.

Jeremy Cherfas
Head, HDRA Department of Genetic Resources
Ryton-on-Dunsmore, Coventry, CV8 3LG

Oriental Vegetables

In the 1993 edition of The Vegetable Finder we published a compendium of the different names under which many of the increasingly popular oriental vegetables pass. We also bemoaned the fact that there was so much confusion, which, we said, makes it more difficult than it need be for people to try these unusual and rewarding additions to the kitchen garden.

Bayam *is another name for*	Amaranthus
Bok choy	Headed Chinese Cabbage
Brocoletto	Choy sum
Calaloo	Amaranthus
Celery Cabbage	Headed Chinese Cabbage
Celtuce	Lettuce Stem
Ceylon spinach	Basella
Chinese Celery Cabbage	Pak choi
Chinese Kale	Chinese broccoli
Chinese Leaves	Headed Chinese Cabbage
Chinese leek	Chinese chives
Chinese lettuce	Lettuce Stem
Chinese mustard greens	Mustard greens
Chinese spinach	Amaranthus
Chinese White Cabbage	Pak choi
Chop suey greens	Chrysanthemum greens
Crosnes	Chinese artichoke
Daikon	Radish
Edible oil seed rape	Choy sum
Flat black Pak choi	Rosette Pak choi
Flat Pak choi	Rosette Pak choi
Flowering pak choi	Choy sum
Flowering white cabbage	Choy sum
Gai choy	Mustard greens
Gai lan	Chinese broccoli
Garlic chives	Chinese chives
Gobo	Burdock

So far, nothing much seems to have changed in the seed catalogues. Indeed, it is still easy to find catalogues happily using the vegetable name in one language as a variety name in another language, exactly equivalent to making a big deal of a potato called Pomme de Terre. Having had favourable comments on the original list, we are republishing it here. Thanks are again due to Joy Larkcom for doing all the hard work of sorting these names out.

Hon tsai tai *is another name for*	Purple flowered choy sum
Hong tsoi sum	Purple flowered choy sum
Indian mustard (greens)	Mustard greens
Indian spinach	Basella
Japanese artichoke	Chinese artichocke
Japanese greens	Chrysanthemum greens
Kaai laan tsoi	Chinese broccoli
Kaai tsoi	Mustard greens
Kailan	Chinese broccoli
Kosaitai	Purple flowered choy sum
Leaf Mustard	Mustard greens
Malabar spinach	Basella
Michihili	Headed Chinese Cabbage
Mooli	Radish
Mustard Cabbage	Pak choi
Mustard cabbage	Mustard greens
Mustard Spinach	Komatsuna
Pak tsoi sum	Choy sum
Purple flowered choy sum	Choy sum
Shungiku	Chrysanthemum greens
Spinach mustard	Komatsuna
Taisin	Pak choi
Tasai	Rosette Pak choi
Tatsoi	Rosette Pak choi
White flowering broccoli	Chinese broccoli
Wong Bok	Headed Chinese Cabbage

Supplier Analysis

As with last year's edition, we have broken down the varieties according to whether they are open pollinated or hybrids and then categorised them according to the number of suppliers. The table this year shows almost no change. Open-pollinated and hybrid varieties seem to be very slightly more widely available.

Number of Suppliers	Open Pollinated			F1 hybrids		
	Number	Per Cent	1993%	Number	Per Cent	1993%
1	995	50	53	512	57	63
-25	627	31	30	296	33	28
>5	378	19	17	83	9	9
Totals	2,000	100	100	891	100	100

This year we are adding another kind of analysis. We often say that for most vegetable crops F1 hybrids have little to offer the ordinary gardener. This year, we have looked at how the share of F1s and open-pollinated varieties differs from supplier to supplier. To do that, we put each variety into one of four classes: Open pollinated and unique to one supplier; open pollinated and available from more than one supplier; F1 hybrid and unique to one supplier; and F1 hybrid and available from more than one supplier. Because the number of varieties in the catalogue varies so widely between suppliers, we then expressed each of these numbers as a percentage of the total number of varieties offered. We then sorted the suppliers in descending order, according to the proportion of their list that is made up of F1 hybrids (except for those beyond MAS, who are in alphabetical order). The results are shown on the next two pages. (We have also placed a magnified version of each supplier's results alongside their entry in the back of the book.)

The most striking result is that the top three for proportion of F1s are also the top three for proportion of unique F1s. Number four has a slightly smaller proportion of unique F1s than number five. And the top four are all seedsmen who supply professional growers exclusively. Draw your own conclusions.

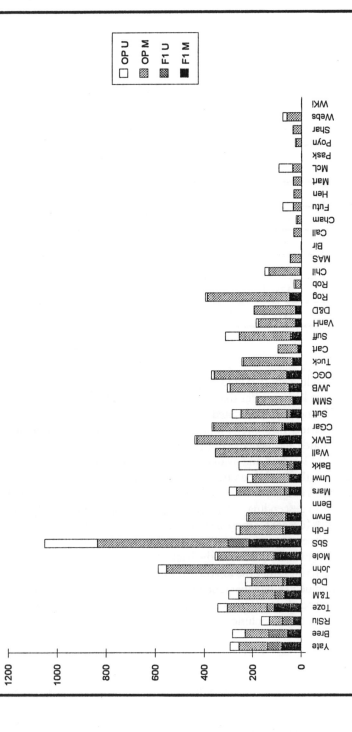

Number of Open Pollinated and F1 varieties

Legend: OP U, OP M, F1 U, F1 M

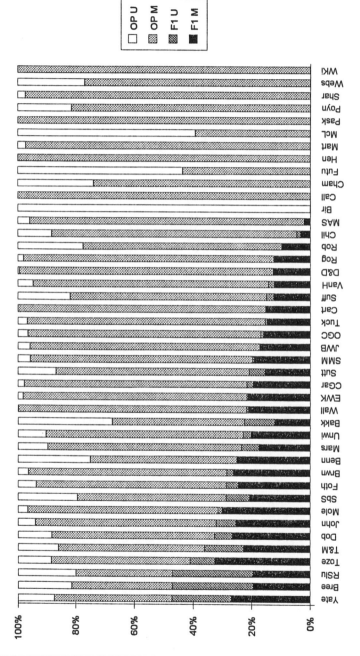

Proportion of Open Pollinated and F1 varieties

Legend: OP U, OP M, F1 U, F1 M

Amaranth (Grain)

Amaranthus spp.
One of the Lost Crops of the Incas. They are fast growing annuals that often reach 2 m. under good conditions. The flower heads are striking and a variety of colours. The seeds are small but nutritious, packed with lysine, which cereals lack. The leaves are also edible, and can be eaten like spinach. Cultivation similar to sweetcorn, although amaranth is more drought tolerant than corn. More work is probably needed before grain amaranth is reliable in our climate, but well worth a try.

Burgundy
Dark purple foliage, red seed heads. (Futu)
FUTU

Golden
Earliest maturing strain, yellow seed heads. (Futu)
FUTU

Multicolor
Foliage is a mixture of red, green and yellow, flowerheads show similar variation. (Futu)
FUTU

Temuco
A variety with small, white, non-bitter seeds that require little washing. Flowerheads are either bright red or bright green. (Futu)
FUTU

Amaranth (Leaf)

Amaranthus gangeticus; also A.dubius, A. mangostanus, A. spinosus
Although the leaves of Grain Amaranth are edible, those of Leaf Amaranths are especially nutritious. There is great variation in leaf shape and colour. A sunny, sheltered site is of benefit.

Hijau Salad Amaranth
Amaranthus mangostanus. An excellent variety, with rounded, lime-green leaves which can be eaten raw or lightly cooked. Amaranth greens are high in minerals and contain 10-15% protein. (Futu)
FUTU

Quintonil
A leaf amaranth from the mountains of southern Mexico, which is used like spinach and said to have a delicious flavour when properly prepared. This variety is grown at high altitudes and is tolerant of rain and cool temperatures. (Futu)
FUTU

Artichoke

Vegetable Amaranth
Red leaf 50 days. Oval heart shaped green leaves overlaid with burgundy (like a coleus) 12-18 in. bushy plant. Much more tolerant than spinach to warm soil. May be cooked like spinach and makes a flavourful addition to salads and stir fry. (Suff)
> CHIL; OGC; SUFF

Artichoke
Cynara scolymus
A relative of the thistle. It is the fleshy bracts of the unopened flower heads that are eaten, and the plants look very good in a decorative border.

Green Ball
This variety is grown for the large fleshy scales or bracts on the flower heads, which can be boiled in salted water. Young plants will produce usable heads in the second year. (Dob)
> DOB

Green Globe
A gourmet variety. Harvest the large flower heads while the fleshy scales are still packed tight. Boil until tender and serve with melted butter. (Unwi)
> BRWN; CGAR; CHIL; D&D; EWK; FOTH; JOHN; JWB; MARS; MOLE; OGC; ROG; SBS; SMM; SUTT; TUCK; WALL

Green Globe Improved
With sharp spines greatly reduced and larger, heavier bearing, consistent quality globe-shaped heads, this is a much improved variety. (T&M)
> T&M

Purple Globe
For those who like "haute cuisine". The thick, fleshy artichoke bottoms can be prepared in several ways. The globe artichoke is a very decorative garden plant that flowers beautifully with large, purple flowers. It should be planted in a sunny sheltered position and be protected in winter. (Bakk)
> BAKK; CGAR; EWK; OGC; ROG; SBS; SMM; VANH; WALL

Vert de Laon
One of the most suitable for cultivation in the UK. Its flavour is judged to be superior to imported artichokes. It gained an award of merit in the RHS trials. (Benn)
> BENN

Violetta di Chioggia
A luxury vegetable that is easily raised from seed. This variety produces a delicious
and attractive purple headed artichoke. Decorative enough for the flower border.
Select the best plants and propagate by division. (Some heads will be green from
this seed). (Suff)
> SUFF

Asparagus
Asparagus officinalis
One of the few edible members of the Lily family. The Emperor Augustus was very partial
to asparagus, which has been grown as a food plant since 200 BC. New all-male hybrids
may be more productive.

F1 Accell
> EWK; OGC; ROG; SBS; SMM; SUFF

F1 Andreas
> DOB

Argenteuil Purple Imported
> SBS

F1 Boonlim
> BENN; RSLU; SMM; T&M

Cito
This French variety has consistently given outstanding results with yields of over
0.5 lb per crown. Longer spears than traditional varieties that are just as tasty and
tender. A light crop may be harvested during the first year. Quite delicious. (Foth)
> FOTH; SUTT

Connover's Colossal
This is an excellent standard variety which is an early and heavy cropper. Being
open pollinated you get more seed for your money but have to wait an extra season
for the first crop. (Suff)
> BENN; BRWN; CGAR; CHIL; D&D; DOB; EWK; JOHN; JWB; MARS; MOLE; OGC;
> ROG; SBS; SMM; SUFF; TUCK; UNWI; VANH; WALL; YATE

F1 Franklim
> JOHN; MARS; RSLU

F1 Gijnlim
> RSLU

Asparagus Pea

F1 Limbras
A remarkable new asparagus genetically polyploid which means the plant naturally produces much thicker shoots often double the size of normal varieties. It can be relied on to produce tender and succulent stems and significantly bigger spears. (T&M)
> CGAR; UNWI

Limburgia
Excellent asparagus with a mild flavour. Limburgia is as soft as butter and not stringy. High yield. (Bakk)
> BAKK

Lucullus
The first all-male variety, it produces a much heavier crop than older varieties where the female plants are weakened by seed-bearing. The spears are longer, slimmer and straighter. (Mars)
> BENN; MARS

Mary Washington
A very strong growing and productive strain producing long, thick spears in May and early June. (T&M)
> ROG; SBS; T&M

Merrygreen
Green asparagus, very tender. Thick spears. Grows without earthing up. Very agreeable flavour. (Bakk)
> BAKK

F1 Rekord
> YATE

F1 Venlim
> SMM

Asparagus Pea
Psophocarpous tetraglonobus
A member of the Legume family, with delightful brick-red flowers. The pods should be picked very small, before they toughen.

Asparagus Pea
> CGAR; CHAM; DOB; EWK; FOTH; FUTU; JWB; OGC; SBS; SMM; SUFF; T&M; TUCK; WALL

Aubergine
Solanum melongena
Also known as the eggplant, and a relative of the tomato and potato. Usually grown with some protection for reliable cropping in the U.K.

Bambino
A true genetic baby vegetable with super early maturity, growing only 12ins tall. Before you know it you will have lots of large, attractive lavender flowers and then clusters of shiny 1inch fruits. These thumb-sized fruits are delicious popped under the grill for a couple of minutes and served hot or can be used in many ways. Excellent plant for container culture or the small garden, wherever space is limited. (T&M)
T&M

Black Beauty
Excellent, open-pollinated variety. Dark purple-black, pear-shaped fruits of good flavour. (Foth)
FOTH; JOHN; MOLE; ROG; SBS

F1 Black Enorma
T&M

F1 Black Prince
T&M

F1 Black bell
JOHN; YATE

F1 Bonica
BRWN; DOB; FOTH; SBS

F1 Dobrix
TOZE

F1 Dusky
SUTT

F1 Easter Egg
JOHN

F1 Elondo
T&M

F1 Large Fruited Slice-Rite
MARS

Basella

Long Purple
Very easy to cultivate, preferably in a warm, sunny position. It will give a high yield of beautiful, purple fruit. (Bakk)
BAKK; CGAR; CHIL; D&D; EWK; JWB; OGC; ROG; SBS; TUCK; VANH; WALL

F1 Long Tom
CGAR; OGC; ROG; SBS

F1 Moneymaker
EWK; FOTH; MOLE; ROG; SBS; SUTT; TOZE; WALL

New York Purple
JOHN

New York Round Purple
SBS

F1 Onita
SUFF

F1 Ovana
SUTT

F1 Palomo
SBS

F1 Rima
BREE

F1 Short Tom
ROG; SBS; SUFF

F1 Slice Rite
ROG; SBS; TUCK

Slice Rite 23
The large, black, oblong fruits can weigh as much as 500g/1lb. Very heavy cropper. (Unwi)
UNWI

F1 Vista
BAKK

Basella

Basella rubra; also B. alba, B. cordifolia
Also known as Ceylon Spinach and Indian Spinach, the leaves, leaf stalks and stems all have a very mild spinach flavour. Very tender, it will not stand any frost, and grows much more rapidly after midsummer.

Indian Spinach
Not a variety name, but an alternative for Basella.
OGC; SUFF

Bath Asparagus

Ornithogalum pyrenaicum
A beautiful and rare native of woods and hedge banks in southern Britain. The unopened flower stalks were gathered at one time and used as an asparagus substitute in the Bath area (hence the name), as well as in Bedfordshire. Likes heavy soils and will tolerate some shade.

Bath Asparagus
FUTU

Bean Other

Extra Early Ben Yard Long Bean
Vigna uniquiculata. Eaten as far afield as India and the West Indies, this giant, novel bean can be grown successfully in a greenhouse in the British Isles. (Foth)
FOTH

Liana Asparagus Bean
A novelty item recommended for growing in a greenhouse or maybe in a warm sheltered position outside in the Southern counties. The long (15-24in.) pods are slim and best cooked cut into 1 inch pieces. The name Asparagus Bean refers to its delicious flavour. (John)
JOHN; ROG; SMM

Yard Long Bean
An interesting variety that can reach 8ft in height with pods that grow to 18in long. Harvest pods when they are the thickness of a pencil. (OGC)
OGC; SUFF

Beetberry

Chenopodium foliosum
An annual, similar to fat hen in appearance, which bears numerous sweet red fruits in the leaf axils which taste rather like bland mulberries, good mixed with other fruits in pies, fruit salads &c. A fun plant, popular with children, and unusual in that it is one of the few berry-bearing members of the family. The leaves can also be eaten like spinach. Vigorous plants which self-seed easily.

Beetberry
FUTU

Beetroot

Beta vulgaris var. conditiva
Related to Swiss Chard and Mangels. Normally grown for the swollen roots, although the leaves are also good to eat.

F1 Action
MARS

Albina Vereduna
(Formerly Snowhite) The ice-white flesh has a sweet flavour surpassing red beetroot, and the curled and wavy leaf is a vegetable delicacy high in vitamins. (T&M)
T&M

Avon Early
SBS

Barbietola di Chioggia
(Beetroot of Chioggia) An old traditional Italian beet. An excellent variety with unusual white rings when the beet is sliced. Cooks to pale pink. Lovely mild flavour. (Suff)
CHIL; MARS; OGC; SUFF

Bikores
The most bolt resistant variety. Bred for fresh market quality, internal colour is excellent. Bikores can be used for both early and late crops. (Brwn)
BRWN; EWK; JOHN; MOLE; SBS; WALL

Boldet
Bred to combine uniform shape, smooth skin and resistance to bolting with the good internal colour. A bold early variety. (Toze)
TOZE

Boltardy
Globe - good colour and flavour. Resistant to bolting. Can be sown earlier than most beetroots, but make sure that the soil has warmed up by using cloches. Otherwise sow late April to July. Crops August to November. (D&D)
BREE; BRWN; CART; CGAR; CHIL; D&D; DOB; EWK; FOTH; JOHN; JWB; MARS; MOLE; OGC; ROG; SBS; SMM; SUTT; T&M; TOZE; TUCK; UNWI; VANH; WALL; YATE

Bonel
Definitely one both for devoted beetroot lovers and first time growers, you won't be disappointed. It is a lovely globe variety with marvellous internal colour and superb succulence. High yields, excellent bolt resistance and long cropping make this exceptional. (Foth)
FOTH

Boston
Smooth skinned round beets with excellent internal colour. Slow bolting. (Toze)
TOZE

Bull's Blood
A real old variety which is grown especially for its spectacular red/purple leaves.
Best picked young. (Suff)
SBS; SUFF

F1 Burpees Golden
CGAR; CHIL; D&D; DOB; EWK; JOHN; JWB; OGC; ROG; SBS; SMM; SUFF;
SUTT; T&M; TUCK; UNWI

Cheltenham Green Top
A broad-shouldered, long-rooted, medium-sized variety. (Dob)
CGAR; DOB; EWK; JOHN; JWB; MAS; MOLE; ROG; SBS; SBS; SUFF; TOZE;
WALL

Cheltenham Mono
Broad shouldered long beet, perfect for storing. Each seed cluster produces only
one seedling. (Mars)
MARS; SBS; TOZE

Crimson Globe see Detroit
Crimson Intermediate see Cylindra
Crimson King
Smooth skin and deep red flesh, circular in shape and of fine flavour and appear-
ance. Keeps well. (OGC)
CGAR; EWK; OGC; ROG; SBS; VANH

Cylindra
Grows above ground in a cylindrical shape. Good flavour. Harvest young. (D&D)
BRWN; EWK; JOHN; JWB; MARS; ROG; SBS; SUFF; T&M; TUCK; UNWI; VANH

D'Egypte see Egyptian Turnip Rooted
Detroit
A fine globe beet for general use. Excellent colour and taste. (Tuck)
CGAR; MAS; MOLE; OGC; SBS; SMM; SUFF; TUCK; VANH

Detroit 2
A small, ball-shaped dark red beet. A wonderful flavour and ideal for bottling,
pickling, freezing. (Foth)
BRWN; CART; DOB; MARS; SUTT; T&M

Detroit 2 Dark Red
BAKK

Beetroot

Detroit 2 Ideal
SBS

Detroit 2 Little Ball
A small, ball-shaped dark red beet. A wonderful flavour and ideal for bottling, pickling, freezing. (Foth)
CGAR; D&D; DOB; EWK; FOTH; ROG; SBS; SUTT; VANH; WALL

Detroit 2 Nero
RSLU

Detroit 2 New Globe
Very productive with roots of exceptional quality and uniformity suitable for all uses. (Bree)
BREE; DOB; JOHN; SBS; YATE

Detroit 2 Spinel
Very uniform baby beets ideal at 1.5ins. diameter but remaining tender, true and tasty when bigger even late in the season. Ideal for pickling or canning and preferred by top restaurants. (T&M)
T&M

Detroit 6 Rubidus
RSLU; T&M

Detroit Crimson Globe
Recommended for all purposes, nice quality. (JWB)
JOHN; JWB

Detroit Globe
Large sized roots for maincrop use. Very suitable for exhibition. (EWK)
CHIL; EWK; ROG; WALL

Detroit Loki
Special, bolt resistant selection of the well-known "Detroit" beetroot with smooth-skinned, deep red, globe-shaped roots and tender flesh which cooks quickly. Delicious harvested small, yet also stores well. (Bakk)
BAKK

Dragon
A medium early Detroit type with round roots, a smooth skin and small tops. The roots are uniform in shape and size with a dark red internal colour and no white rings. Good bolt resistance for a Detroit type and particularly suitable for freezing. (Foth)
FOTH

Dwergina
A short topped Detroit type with intense colour, smooth texture and superb sweet flavour. Remains quite small even at maturity. (Suff)
CHIL; JWB; OGC; SBS; SUFF; VANH

Egyptian Flat see Egyptian Turnip Rooted
Egyptian Turnip Rooted
Smooth flattish-round roots have beautifully coloured deep red flesh and an exceptionally fine flavour. (Bakk)
BAKK; SBS

Extra Early Globe see Detroit
Forono
Improved intermediate type. Half long stump ended roots of extra good flavour. (EWK)
BAKK; DOB; EWK; FOTH; OGC; SBS; SMM; SUTT

Globe see Detroit
Golden see Burpees Golden
Golden Ball
SBS; WALL

Kogel
Our most popular round variety. Good deep red, excellent choice for table use and ideal for all exhibition work. Sow early March to May on all soils. (VanH)
VANH

Kyros
Excellent winter food for animals in the winter. (JWB)
JWB; MAS

Libero
Very quick growing main crop variety. Tender, tasty roots that can be sown through to mid-summer. (EWK)
CGAR; EWK; ROG; SBS; VANH; WALL

Lola
A very early globe with strong resistance to bolting. For the earliest crop of young beetroot in June, sow 3 seed cluster per section in modules in February. Raise in a cool greenhouse and do not thin the seedlings. Harden off and plant out the groups of seedlings when they about 2ins high, each group ten inches apart. (Mars)
MARS

Mammoth Long
CGAR; ROB; WALL

Beetroot

Monaco
Smooth-skinned globe Beetroot with uniform internal coloration. Fine flavoured variety. (Dob)
DOB

F1 Moneta
SUTT; TUCK

Monodet
Produces only one seedling from each seed cluster, reducing the amount of thinning required. Globe roots, crimson-fleshed, free from rings. Good bolt resistance. (Mars)
MARS; SBS; TOZE

Monogram
An excellent dark red, well flavoured globe beet with good vigour, smooth skin and superb rich red colour when sliced. Each seed produces only one seedling. (T&M)
JOHN; T&M; TOZE; UNWI

Monopoly
Outstanding variety derived from and having the qualities of Boltardy. Each seed produces only one seedling. (T&M)
BREE; CART; DOB; FOTH; JWB; SBS; T&M

Nobol
SBS

F1 Pablo
BRWN; SUTT; TOZE; VANH

Pronto
MOLE; WALL

Ran Uniball
Suitable for early, main and second crop-production. Quick growing, bolting-resistant and giving very good yields of uniform beets. (Bree)
BREE; SBS

F1 Red Ace
CGAR; FOTH; JOHN; ROB; SUTT; T&M

Regala
The best round Detroit type for early sowing. The deep red beet, with rings, have comparatively little foliage and store particularly well. (Unwi)
JOHN; UNWI

Replata
Very early. Quality outstanding. Very resistant to bolting. (Mars)
MOLE; SBS; T&M

Rubigala
SBS

Slowbolt
SBS

Snowhite see Albina Vereduna
F1 Sprinter
YATE

Broad Bean
Vicia faba
Very hardy beans, often overwintered.

Acme see Masterpiece Green Longpod
Aguadulce
JOHN

Aquadulce Claudia
Very hardy variety for early spring or autumn sowing. Medium long pods with white beans. Ideal for freezing. (EWK)
BREE; CART; CGAR; D&D; DOB; EWK; FOTH; JOHN; JWB; MARS; MAS; MOLE; OGC; ROG; RSLU; SBS; SMM; SUTT; T&M; TOZE; TUCK; VANH; WALL; YATE

Aquadulce Loreta
A vigorous, early autumn or early spring sowing type. Ready 1 week before Aguadulce, producing well-filled pods with 7 delicious beans per pod. Excellent vigour and frost resistance. (T&M)
T&M

Bonny Lad
This is excellent for small gardens. The plants are from 15-18 in. high and produce 3 or 4 stems each bearing a cluster of smooth, 5 in. long pods. (Dob)
CART; DOB

Brandy
A white seeded variety with medium small seeds bred specifically for processing, but which is also an excellent all purpose variety. Brandy has a high seed to pod ratio. (Bree)
BREE

Broad Bean

Bunyards Exhibition
Difficult to beat for all-round performance. Crops heavily with "long-pod" beans full of flavour. Good for autumn or spring sowing. (Foth)
CART; CGAR; EWK; FOTH; JOHN; MAS; MOLE; OGC; ROG; SBS; SHAR; SMM; UNWI; VANH; WALL

Cavalier
ROG

Colossal see Conqueror
Conqueror
Long pods widely used for exhibition. Plump beans of excellent flavour. (Sutt)
MOLE

Dreadnought
Outstanding quality for late spring sowing. Sturdy quick growing plants with good size pods. (EWK)
BREE; BRWN; CGAR; CHIL; DOB; EWK; JOHN; MAS; ROG; SBS; SMM; SUTT; WALL; YATE

Express
Fast to mature from early spring sowings, this heavy cropper has recorded a maximum of 34 saleable pods per plant in commercial use. Good for freezing. (OGC)
CGAR; DOB; EWK; JOHN; MARS; OGC; ROG; RSLU; SBS; SHAR; SMM; SUFF; T&M; TOZE

Feligreen
Shorter in growth and more wind-resistant than other varieties. The beans retain their deep green colour and exceptional flavour when frozen. (Mars)
MARS

Futura
A bicolour flowering bean with a large, slightly curved pods which ripen evenly and contain four to five beans. A little shorter and more robust than other white seeded varieties. It is one of the earliest spring sown varieties; early to mature from and early spring sowing. Reaches a full grown height of 2 ft. 6 in. (Foth)
FOTH; MOLE

Giant Exhibition Longpod see Dreadnought
Giant Four Seeded Green Windsor
JOHN

Giant Four Seeded White Windsor
JOHN

Green Longpod
A hardy green broad bean for overwinter or early use. Well filled pods with up to nine beans in each, can reach 12in. and more. (OGC)
   OGC

Green Windsor
Large seeded with excellent flavour, this variety freezes well. (OGC)
   D&D; EWK; OGC; Rog; SbS; Suff; Wall

Hylon
An outstanding variety producing pods of great length. Freezes well and highly recommended for exhibition. (Sutt)
   JWB; Rog; Shar; Sutt; Tuck; Yate

Imperial Green Longpod
Produces pods some 15in. long, each containing up to 9 large, green beans. (Dob)
   Dob; Foth; John; Rog; T&M; Toze

Imperial Green Windsor
Deep green colour, excellent cropper. (CGar)
   CGar; John; Rog; Shar

Imperial White Longpod
Extremely long, broad pods containing 9 to 10 beans. Excellent for exhibition. (Mars)
   John; Mars; Rog; Unwi

Imperial White Windsor
Long podded with well-filled pods. Seeds are good size. (Sutt)
   Cart; John; Rog; Sutt

Irago
   Toze

Ite Beryl
A well-known white seeded processing variety where it is used because of its small seeds. Beryl has few rivals for size, plant type and lateness. (Bree)
   Bree; Shar

Jade
Developed from Feligreen, it gives a heavy crop of light green beans which retain their colour after cooking. The smaller size of the beans makes them ideal for freezing. Sturdy plants, shorter than most, with upright pods. (Mars)
   Mars

Johnson's Wonderful
An early longpod type giving a heavy yield of good quality beans. (OGC)
   OGC; Rog; SbS

Broad Bean

Jubilee Hysor
Up to 9 large succulent white beans much more closely packed into the pods than usual, thereby making shelling faster and easier. (Dob)
> Dob; Foth; Mars; Rog; Shar

Masterpiece Green Longpod
Excellent length of pod and table quality. A fine green-seeded broad bean and also excellent for deep freezing. (Sutt)
> Brwn; Cart; CGar; Chil; D&D; EWK; John; JWB; Mole; Rog; RSlu; SbS; Shar; Sutt; Tuck; Unwi; VanH; Wall; Yate

Medes
> Rog; Shar

Meteor
One of the earliest varieties producing a heavy crop of long pods (Length approx. 20 cm.). A brown-cooking bean with the specific broad bean flavour. It is resistant to diseases. (Bakk)
> Bakk

Metissa
Fine-seeded broad bean. This white-flowering variety is insensitive to unfavourable weather conditions. Metissa is a strong broad bean which, in addition, offers a surprisingly high yield. (Bakk)
> Bakk; Shar

Minica
A high yielding Express type with 4-5 tiny beans per pod. Excellent for freezing. (OGC)
> OGC; Rog

Red Epicure
A fine long pod of exhibition standard, with deep chestnut-crimson seeds. Some of the colour is lost in cooking, but it still retains the superb flavour. (Unwi)
> Unwi

Relon
Produces an abundance of long, plump pods containing an average of 8-9 green seeds of excellent quality and flavour. Of tallish habit, a vigorous and most reliable variety. (Dob)
> Dob; Rog; Shar; Sutt

Statissa
Bronze seeded variety with true broad bean flavour. Consistently outyielded Express and other heavy yielding varieties. It averages 4 mid-size beans per 5in. pod. Early. (T&M)
> Rog; T&M; Toze

Superaguadulce

Largely used for autumn sowing, earlier and more compact than the English strain, and we consider this the largest podded variety in its class. (Brwn)

BRWN; SHAR

The Sutton

A compact and bushy variety, little over 1ft high, ideal for small gardens. Excellent flavour. (Mars)

BRWN; CGAR; D&D; EWK; FOTH; JOHN; JWB; MARS; MOLE; OGC; ROG; SHAR; SMM; SUFF; SUTT; T&M; TUCK; UNWI; VANH; WALL

Threefold White

An excellent variety widely used by the canning and freezing industry. The pods are about 6-7 in. long and the beans are smaller than most other varieties, with a white eye. It is a spring sowing variety. Height 3-3.5 ft. (John)

BAKK; JOHN; JWB

Topic

SUTT

White Windsor

Will not stand frost, so must not be planted out or sown in the open until all danger of frost is past. (OGC)

D&D; EWK; JWB; OGC; ROG; SBS

Witkiem see Meteor

Witkiem Major

A very fast and early variety giving large yields of long, thick pods. A little after Vroma. (Foth)

CGAR; D&D; EWK; MOLE; ROG; T&M; TOZE; UNWI; VANH

Witkiem Manita

An early maturing variety suitable for early spring sowings. (Bree)

BREE; BRWN; JOHN; OGC; ROG; SHAR; YATE

Witkiem Vroma

An excellent spring sowing variety, it is early enough to crop at the same time as autumn sown varieties without lost yield. Good harvests of medium-size pods containing 5 or 6 white seeds. (Foth)

DOB; FOTH; MARS

Broccoli

Brassica olearacea convar. botrytis Alef. var. cymosa

A brassica grown for the flower heads, this classification also includes calabrese and sprouting broccoli.

Broccoli

F1 Adriatic
SbS

F1 Arcadia
Bree; John; Yate

Autumn Calabrese
Large green "heads" followed by side shoots. (Unwi)
Unwi

Autumn Spear
An abundance of delicious green spears from September to November. (Sutt)
Sutt

Broccoletto
A speciality from Italy. A quick sweet flavoured broccoli producing a single head at about 9 in. tall. (OGC)
OGC; Suff

F1 Cape Queen
SbS

F1 Caravel
RSlu; T&M

F1 Chancellor
SbS

F1 Citation
Dob

F1 Comanche
Bree

F1 Corvet
Brwn; Cart; CGar; D&D; Dob; EWK; Foth; John; JWB; Mole; OGC; Rog; RSlu; SbS; Suff; T&M; Tuck; Unwi; Wall

F1 Cruiser
John; Mole; RSlu

F1 Dandy
SbS

Dandy Early
Vigorous and extra early. Up to 10 oz., 5.5 in. very firm deep green heads. (T&M)
T&M

De Cicco see Ramoso calabrese
F1 Delicia
Bree

F1 Dundee
YATE

El Centro
Produces a good crop of side-shoots over a lengthy harvesting period. (Mars)
MARS

F1 Emerald City
YATE

F1 Emperor
FOTH; OGC; SBS; TOZE; UNWI

F1 Eusebio
JOHN

F1 Express Corona
SUTT

F1 Floccoli
T&M

F1 Ginga
BREE; YATE

F1 Green Belt
BREE; JOHN; SBS; TOZE; YATE

F1 Green Comet
BRWN; EWK; FOTH; JWB; MOLE; ROG; SBS; SMM; T&M; WALL

F1 Green Duke
JOHN; JWB; SBS

Green Sprouting
Medium-sized central heads produced in summer followed by a profusion of sprouts.
Do not sow later than mid-May. (Dob)
BAKK; CART; CGAR; CHIL; D&D; DOB; EWK; FOTH; JOHN; JWB; MOLE; OGC;
ROG; SBS; SUFF; VANH; WALL

F1 Green Valiant
JOHN

F1 Lancelot
YATE

F1 Laser
RSLU

F1 Legend
BREE

Broccoli

F1 Marathon
BREE; JOHN; TOZE; TUCK; YATE

F1 Mercedes
BREE; JWB; MARS; OGC; SBS

Mirage
Very high yielding Calabrese type with pale green heads and small beads. (Suff)
SUFF

Morse's 4638
SBS

F1 Neptune
RSLU

Nine Star Perennial
Multi-heading variety; will produce up to ten small white heads from each plant.
(EWK)
CGAR; CHIL; DOB; EWK; FOTH; JWB; MARS; MOLE; ROG; SBS; SUTT; VANH;
WALL

F1 Northern Dancer
FOTH

Pacifica
A general purpose non-hybrid mid-season variety. Not as uniform as the F1 hybrids and gives a spread of cropping over several weeks. (Toze)
TOZE

F1 Packman
SBS; TOZE; YATE

F1 Pinnacle
SBS

F1 Pirate
SBS

F1 Premium Crop
SBS; TOZE

F1 Prima
SBS

F1 Prominence
BREE

Purple Sprouting
Produces delicious purple flowered shoots in great profusion as early as February.
High in vitamin B. (Suff)
CGAR; CHIL; D&D; EWK; MOLE; ROG; SMM; SUFF; SUTT; UNWI; VANH

Purple Sprouting Early
Extremely hardy and will provide a succession of delicious tender shoots. Easy to grow. (Foth)
> Bree; Brwn; Cart; Dob; Foth; John; JWB; Mars; OGC; RSlu; SbS; Toze; Tuck; Wall; Yate

Purple Sprouting Late
April heading. (OGC)
> Bree; Brwn; EWK; John; JWB; Mars; OGC; RSlu; SbS; Suff; T&M; Toze

Purple Sprouting Red Spear
A newly introduced early variety, producing fine quality spears. (Brwn)
> Brwn

Ramoso
(De Cicco). This is an old Italian variety for spring or autumn cropping. Non-uniform in maturity and producing over a long season. After the main head is cut a large yield of spears (side shoots) is produced. Delicious and tender. (Suff)
> Suff

Red Arrow
A vast improvement on existing strains, cropping 1 week earlier and yielding up to 20% more. Vigorous plants producing lots of vitamin rich, tender flower buds. (T&M)
> Dob; OGC; T&M; Toze

Red Lion
Purple headed variety to mature in the autumn. Produces deep, well coloured heads that are well protected. (Toze)
> Toze

F1 Regilio
> Mole; Wall

Romanesco
A very distinctive type of broccoli, maturing in late autumn. Lime-green heads up to 6 in. across, consisting of many "pinnacles" of curd. Extremely soft. texture and magnificent flavour. For May sowing only. (Mars)
> Cart; CGar; Chil; D&D; Dob; EWK; JWB; Mars; OGC; Rog; SbS; Suff; Sutt; Unwi; VanH; Wall

F1 Roxie
> Yate

F1 Royal Banquet
> Unwi

Broccoli

F1 SG1
SᴮS

F1 Samurai
Bʀᴇᴇ; Jᴏʜɴ; SᴮS; Tᴏᴢᴇ; Yᴀᴛᴇ

F1 Septal SC
SᴮS

F1 Shogun
Bʀᴇᴇ; CGᴀʀ; D&D; EWK; Fᴏᴛʜ; Jᴏʜɴ; Mᴏʟᴇ; OGC; SᴮS; SMM; Sᴜꜰꜰ; Tᴏᴢᴇ; Tᴜᴄᴋ; Yᴀᴛᴇ

F1 Skiff
RSʟᴜ; SᴮS

F1 Southern Comet
Bᴀᴋᴋ; Mᴏʟᴇ; SᴮS; Tᴏᴢᴇ

F1 Sprinter
Jᴏʜɴ

F1 Stolto
SᴮS

F1 Sumosun
VᴀɴH

F1 Topstar
Uɴᴡɪ

F1 Trixie
Mᴀʀs; T&M; Uɴᴡɪ

F1 Vantage
EWK; SᴮS

White Sprouting
Delicious shoots like tiny cauliflowers are produced when vegetables of this type are usually scarce. (Bree)
Bʀᴇᴇ; Cᴀʀᴛ; CGᴀʀ; Cʜɪʟ; D&D; EWK; Mᴏʟᴇ; OGC; Rᴏɢ; SMM

White Sprouting Early
Ready March when there are few other vegetables. Very hardy. (Mars)
Fᴏᴛʜ; Jᴏʜɴ; JWB; Mᴀʀs; MAS; RSʟᴜ; SᴮS; Sᴜꜰꜰ; Tᴏᴢᴇ; Tᴜᴄᴋ; Uɴᴡɪ; VᴀɴH; Wᴀʟʟ; Yᴀᴛᴇ

White Sprouting Improved
Delicious creamy-white shoots for use in March-April. (Sutt)
   SUTT

White Sprouting Late
Pure white "mini cauliflowers" holding into May. (Mars)
   BRWN; DOB; EWK; JOHN; JWB; MARS; MAS; RSLU; SBS; TOZE

White Star
Stock has been rigorously re-selected to give higher yields than existing strains plus a much higher quality spear. (T&M)
   T&M; TOZE

Brussels Sprout

Brassica oleracea convar. oleracea
The sprouts are swollen buds on the stem, and a good firm soil is needed to ensure that they do not become too loose.

F1 7159
   TOZE

F1 Acropolis
   MOLE; RSLU; SBS

F1 Adeline
   JOHN; SBS

F1 Adonis
   BREE; T&M

F1 Ajax
   BREE

F1 Annette
   YATE

F1 Aries
   MOLE; SBS

Ashwell Strain
Produces good, firm sprouts. (JWB)
   JOHN; JWB

Bedford
For picking between December and February. Plants of medium height closely packed with firm, dark green sprouts of fine flavour. (Dob)
   DOB

Brussels Sprout

Bedford Blue Vein
A late sprout which stands well and produces a large crop of dark green sprouts on tall stems. (Suff)
CGar; EWK; JWB; Rog; SbS; Suff; Wall

Bedford Darkmar 21
Lots of firm sprouts with a fine flavour. (Foth)
Brwn; Foth; John; JWB; Mole; OGC; SbS; Tuck; VanH; Wall; Yate

Bedford Fillbasket
A open pollinated sprout producing large solid buttons from October to December. (Suff)
CGar; Chil; EWK; Rog; SbS; Suff; Sutt; VanH; Wall

Bedford Winter Harvest
Dark green medium-sized sprouts from October to February. Strong, very hardy plants. (Sutt)
Sutt

F1 Boxer
Mole; SbS

F1 Buttons
Foth

Cambridge No 1
A very early sprout of excellent flavour. (JWB)
CGar; JWB

Cambridge No 5
Large sprouts - ready December/January. (D&D)
CGar; D&D; EWK; John; MAS; OGC; Rog; SbS; SMM; Suff; Wall

F1 Caroline
Bakk

F1 Cascade
Dob; John

F1 Cavalier
John; Mole; SbS; T&M; Toze; Wall

F1 Citadel
Cart; CGar; Dob; EWK; Foth; JWB; Rog; SbS; SMM; Sutt; T&M; VanH; Wall

F1 Claudette
EWK; OGC; SbS; Yate

F1 Content
SbS

F1 Cor Valiant
Bree; CGar; Mole; Rog; SbS; SMM; Wall

F1 Corinth
Bree

F1 Diablo
Brwn

F1 Dolmic
John; Mole; RSlu; T&M

F1 Domica
SbS

Early Half Tall
A very early variety which gives a heavy crop of buttons from top to bottom of the stalk. Should be ready from September and should stand throughout November. (OGC)
John; Mole; OGC; SbS; Wall

F1 Edmund
Bree; SbS; Toze

Evesham Special
A good, well-established variety with firm, early crops. Large, tasty sprouts on medium plants. Ideal for growing in exposed positions. (Foth)
Brwn; CGar; Foth; John; MAS; Mole; Rog; SbS; Wall

F1 Fermesse
RSlu

F1 Fortress
D&D; EWK; Foth; John; Mars; OGC; Rog; SbS; SMM; Suff; Tuck; Unwi; VanH; Wall

F1 Gabion
John; RSlu

F1 Gavin
Bree; John; SbS

F1 Golfer
Mole; SbS

F1 HZH021
John

F1 Hossa
SbS

Brussels Sprout

Huizer Laat see Huizer's Late

F1 Hunter
SBS

F1 Icarus
BREE; T&M; WALL

F1 Igor
YATE

F1 Jaqueline
BAKK

F1 Jubilee
SBS

F1 Kundry
BREE

F1 Lancelot
ROG

F1 Lunet
JOHN; MARS; MOLE; RSLU; SBS; WALL

F1 Mallard
A heavy cropping, early to mid-season variety that stands well. Medium-size, solid, dark green sprouts on very erect plants. (Unwi)
JWB; UNWI

F1 Montgomery
BRWN; MARS; TOZE

F1 Nicoline
BAKK

Noisette
An old French variety; gourmet vegetable. Small tight sprouts with very distinctive nutty flavour. (Suff)
OGC; SUFF

F1 Odette
EWK; SBS; T&M; TOZE; YATE

F1 Oliver
BREE; BRWN; JOHN; JWB; SBS; T&M; TOZE

F1 Ormavon
FOTH

F1 Ottoline
JOHN; SBS

F1 Pallas
BREE

F1 Pantera
RSLU

F1 Pauline
JOHN

F1 Peer Gynt
BREE; BRWN; CART; CGAR; D&D; DOB; EWK; FOTH; JOHN; JWB; MARS; MOLE; OGC; ROG; SBS; SMM; SUFF; SUTT; T&M; UNWI; VANH; WALL

F1 Perfect Line
SBS

F1 Philemon
BREE

F1 Predora
MARS; MOLE; SBS; VANH

F1 Prelent
MOLE

F1 Prince Marvel
EWK; ROG; SBS; SMM; WALL

F1 Rampart
BRWN; CGAR; DOB; EWK; JOHN; MOLE; OGC; RSLU; SBS; SMM; SUFF; TOZE; TUCK; UNWI; WALL

Red see Rubine

F1 Richard
BREE; TOZE

F1 Roger
A very widely grown variety which produces very smooth slightly elongated sprouts on a very strong plant. Yields are very high, and standing ability is excellent. (Bree)
BREE; JOHN; JWB; SBS; TOZE; UNWI

Roodnerf
An excellent maincrop, ready from November onward giving a good yield of firm, medium-sized sprouts. Remains sound and can be picked over a long period. (Dob)
DOB

Roodnerf Early Button
High yield of medium-sized sprouts of excellent quality for picking at Christmas. Sprouts keep well on the stem over a long period. (Sutt)
SUTT

Roodnerf Seven Hills see Seven Hills
Roodnerf Stiekema
An excellent variety from which you can harvest all winter long. Beautiful, tight sprouts, excellent quality. (Bakk)
> BAKK

Rous Lench
Dwarf habit, excellent cropper. (JWB)
> JWB; SBS

Rubine
A red sprout to give a little variation to winter vegetables. Excellent flavour and becoming popular in the fresh market. (OGC)
> CHIL; FOTH; JWB; OGC; SBS; SMM; SUFF; WALL

F1 Saxon
> SUTT

Seven Hills
A late Brussels sprout, which will give a bountiful crop ready just after Christmas and will stand through January. (OGC)
> CART; D&D; EWK; FOTH; OGC; ROG; SBS; VANH; WALL

F1 Sheriff
> JOHN; MARS; MOLE; SBS; WALL

F1 Skios
> BREE

F1 Smasher
> VANH

F1 Stan
> ROB; WALL

F1 Stephen
> BREE; JWB; WALL

F1 Stockade
> JWB; SBS

F1 Sultan
> SBS

F1 Tardis
> BREE; SBS; TOZE

F1 Tavernos
> BREE; T&M

The Wroxton
> SBS

Fl Titurel
BREE; SBS

Fl Topaz
SBS

Fl Topline
JOHN; TOZE

Fl Troika
DOB; FOTH; JOHN; SBS

United
Bred by combining the best of Bedfordshire type inbred lines to give a more uniform open pollinated Ashwell's stock. (Toze)
TOZE

Fl Victor
SBS

Fl Welland
MARS

Fl Wellington
FOTH; JOHN; TOZE; UNWI

Fl Widgeon
JWB; MARS; SUTT

Fl Zoras
BREE; TOZE

Buckwheat
Fagopyrum spp
Madawaska Buckwheat
Fagopyrum tartaricum. A native of the Himalayan region, this variety is more drought resistant and tolerates cooler temperatures than normal buckwheat. It grew well for us in 1993 despite bad weather and little attention. Seeds can easily be harvested and ground to make flour which makes tasty buckwheat pancakes. Young leaves can be eaten as a spinach. (Futu)
FUTU

Bulbous rooted Chervil
Chaerophyllum bulbosum
Once grown widely for the roots. Germination is difficult, needing a cold winter. Selection might improve this vegetable with ease.

Burdock

Turnip rooted chervil
FUTU

Burdock

Arctium lappa
Although Burdock grows wild in Europe, in Japan and China it is cultivated as a vegetable. The long roots are the favoured part, although the young leaves can also be eaten. Gobo, often given as a variety name, is the Japanese for burdock.

Burdock
A bushy plant with large leaves and purple thistle like flowers. Blooms July-Sept. An important blood purifier. Has anti-bacterial properties and is used for many skin problems. Useful also for rheumatism and arthritis. The root may be boiled as a vegetable and the stalk, prior to flowering, may also be cooked. Habitat: waste ground. (Suff)
FUTU; SUFF

Greater
CHAM

Lesser
CHAM

Watanabe Early
A very rapid grower, producing long, slender roots about 30ins. long with flesh of a fine texture and of a good flavour. (Chil)
CHIL; JOHN

Cabbage

Brassica oleracea convar. capitata
F1 85F-5
YATE

F1 Advance
TOZE

F1 Advantage
TOZE

Alpha see Golden Acre
F1 Alt 8905
TOZE

F1 Alt 8939
TOZE

Amager
SBS

F1 Anton
BREE

April
Early spring cutting variety forming dwarf compact hearts. (EWK)
BREE; CGAR; EWK; JOHN; JWB; MOLE; ROG; SBS; SUFF; SUTT; TUCK; VANH;
WALL; YATE

F1 Aquila
SBS

F1 Arena
YATE

F1 Aristocrat
SBS; TOZE

F1 Atria
RSLU

Avon Crest
Best of the spring cabbages for standing. (JWB)
JWB; SBS; YATE

F1 Barnaby
YATE

F1 Bartolo
CGAR; JOHN; MOLE; SBS; TOZE

F1 Big Ben
SBS

F1 Bison
JOHN; SBS

Biwama
SBS

F1 Bouchon
SBS

Brunswick
Very large heads for autumn and early winter use. Will stand for a long time without splitting. (EWK)
EWK; JOHN; ROG; SBS; SMM; VANH; WALL

Cabbage

Brunswijker see Brunswick

Budereich
The standard variety for autumn cutting. Solid deep green ballheads weighing up to 3 lbs. Very uniformly shaped therefore most suitable for exhibition work. (VanH)
SBS; VANH

F1 Cape Horn
EWK; FOTH; JWB; SBS; YATE

F1 Carnival
TOZE

F1 Castello
JOHN; MARS; SBS; T&M; TOZE

F1 Charmant
JOHN; TOZE; YATE

Christmas Drumhead
Solid flat-topped hearts. Ready December. (D&D)
CGAR; D&D; DOB; EWK; JOHN; JWB; MARS; MOLE; OGC; ROG; SBS; SMM; SUFF; TOZE; UNWI; VANH; WALL

Christmas Drumhead Early
A blue-green drumhead maturing Oct-Nov from sowings made outdoors April-early May. (Sutt)
SUTT

F1 Clarinet
BREE

Coeur de Boeuf
Medium-early variety. Produces sturdy, high-rounded cabbages of at least 2 kg. on a short stump. Perfect variety for bottling. (Bakk)
BAKK

Coleslaw
Superb quality autumn and early winter cabbage. Fine white heads for shredding, will keep for a long time. (EWK)
CGAR; D&D; EWK

F1 Colt
BREE

F1 Comas
YATE

Copenhagen Market
JOHN; SBS

Cotswold Queen
Somewhat later in maturity than Offenham, this makes better heads. (OGC)
    John; OGC; SbS; Yate

F1 Custodian
    Mole; SbS; Yate

F1 Cutlass
    SbS

Delicatesse
    SbS

F1 Delphi
    John; Mole; RSlu; SbS; Wall

F1 Delus
    RSlu

Derby Day
A tip-top ballhead. Should be ready in early June. (Foth)
    Brwn; CGar; EWK; Foth; John; JWB; Mars; Mole; Rog; SbS; Toze; Tuck; VanH; Wall; Yate

Ditmarscher Forcing see Golden Acre
Dorado
    John; SbS

F1 Duchy
    T&M

F1 Dumas
    RSlu

F1 Duncan
    Brwn; John; Mole; SbS; Toze; Unwi; Wall; Yate

Durham Early
Autumn sowing variety for spring cutting. Small firm hearts of excellent quality and flavour. (EWK)
    Brwn; CGar; EWK; Foth; John; JWB; Mars; MAS; Mole; Rog; SbS; Tuck; Unwi; VanH; Wall

Durham Elf
A small high class selection of Durham Early. (Bree)
    Bree; John; SbS; Yate

Earliest of All
Our own introduction into the commercial market. Excellent ball head type of compact habit and very early to mature. Can be grown at close spacing. (EWK)
    EWK

Cabbage

Early Drumhead see Brunswick
Early Flat Dutch see Brunswick
Early Jersey Wakefield
A very old variety that deserves to be grown more today. Heads are shaped like an upside down ice cream cone, dark waxy green and very compact. Weighing 2-3 lbs. superb eating quality and stands without splitting. May also be sown March/April for cutting during August/Sept. (Suff)
    SMM; SUFF

Early Queen
One of the best Spring Cabbages. Sow in late summer for early Spring Greens or later for tight heads. (Suff)
    EWK; SBS; SUFF

Ellam's Early Dwarf
Good flavoured oval heads for eating March-May. (D&D)
    EWK; JOHN; JWB; ROG; SBS; WALL

F1 Emerald Cross Summer Monarch
    JWB; WALL

F1 Enfield (2811)
    BREE

Enkhuizen Glory
    JOHN; SBS

F1 Erdeno
    BREE

F1 Espoir
    JOHN; TOZE

F1 Eureka
    YATE

Express
A very high-quality selection with little core. Pointed solid heads. (Mars)
    BRWN; CART; CGAR; CHIL; D&D; DOB; FOTH; JWB; MARS; MAS; MOLE; OGC; ROG; SBS; SMM; SUFF; SUTT; TOZE; YATE

Express
F1 Felix
    FOTH

F1 Fidelio
    JOHN

First Early Market 218
A fine large leafy dark green cabbage well suited to the "greens" trade and also for heading. (Bree)
BREE; BRWN; JOHN; MOLE; RSLU; SBS; TOZE; UNWI; YATE

First of June
A dark Primo type. Small head, uniformity and compactness. Can be used for general purpose drilling for succession in the summer. (Toze)
TOZE

F1 Flagship
OGC

F1 Fortune
EWK; SBS

F1 Freshma
EWK; JOHN; SBS; TOZE; YATE

F1 Globe King
SBS

Gloria see Green Boy
Golden Acre
Early cabbage, weighing 1.5 kg. Can be harvested in early summer. (Bakk)
BAKK; BRWN; CGAR; CHIL; D&D; DOB; EWK; FOTH; JOHN; JWB; MARS; MAS; MOLE; OGC; ROG; SBS; SMM; SUTT; TOZE; TUCK; UNWI; VANH; WALL; YATE

Golden Acre Baseball
SBS

Golden Acre Earliest of All
A fast cabbage for late spring and summer use. Matures within 12 weeks. Very firm and delicious for coleslaw or cooked. (Suff)
SBS; SUFF

Golden Acre Extra Early
JOHN; MOLE; SBS

Golden Acre May Express
Fine ballhead maturing 7-8 weeks from planting. Excellent cooked, and also raw shredded in salads and coleslaw. (Sutt)
SBS; SUTT

Golden Acre Primo
JOHN

Golden Acre Progress
Very early variety with small round solid heads. (BREE)
SBS

Cabbage

Golden Acre Rapidity
  SBS

F1 Golden Cross
  BREE; JOHN; JWB; MOLE; TOZE

F1 Goodma
  JOHN; YATE

Gouden Akker see Golden Acre
F1 Green Boy
  SBS

F1 Green Coronet
  EWK; SBS

F1 Green Express
  JOHN; SBS; YATE

Green Sleeves
For early greens to cut before Early Market. This variety bred to reduce the "stalkiness" so common in greens harvested at this period. (Toze)
  TOZE

Green Wonder
  SBS

F1 Grenadier
  BREE

Greyhound
Very early compact pointed hearts, can be grown close together. (EWK)
  EWK; JOHN; TUCK; UNWI; VANH; WALL

Greyhound see Express
Harbinger
  JOHN; SBS

F1 Hawke
  DOB; JWB; SUTT

Herald
A triple purpose type with extra vigour and excellent standing ability. Dependant on when you sow, it will produce, Spring Cabbage, delicious summer greens or autumn cabbage. (T&M)
  T&M

Hercules
The giant cabbage specially bred to produce prize winning heavy weights. (T&M)
  T&M

F1 Hermes
RSʟᴜ

F1 Hidena
Jᴏʜɴ; JWB; SʙS; Tᴏᴢᴇ

F1 Hispi
Very early pointed cabbage variety can still be sown in autumn as well as in early spring. It produces beautiful, tight, uniform cabbages. (Bakk)
Bᴀᴋᴋ; Bʀᴡɴ; Cᴀʀᴛ; CGᴀʀ; D&D; Dᴏʙ; EWK; Fᴏᴛʜ; Jᴏʜɴ; JWB; Mᴏʟᴇ; Rᴏɢ; SʙS; SMM; Sᴜᴛᴛ; T&M; Tᴏᴢᴇ; Tᴜᴄᴋ; Uɴᴡɪ; Wᴀʟʟ

F1 Histona
VᴀɴH

Holland Late Winter
A Dutch white winter cabbage which produces large, firm round heads. Good both cooked or eaten raw in salads and coleslaw. (Foth)
CGᴀʀ; EWK; Fᴏᴛʜ; Jᴏʜɴ; OGC; Rᴏɢ; SʙS; Sᴜᴛᴛ; Tᴜᴄᴋ; Wᴀʟʟ

Holland Late Winter E50
Jᴏʜɴ

Holland Winter
The average weight of these cabbages, which store well for a long time, can be as much as 4-5 kg. Beautiful colour and good flavour. (Bakk)
Bᴀᴋᴋ; JWB

Holland Winter E50 see Langedijk 4
Holland Winter White Extra Late see Langedijk 4
F1 Horizon
RSʟᴜ

F1 Hornet
Bʀᴇᴇ

F1 Hornspi
Jᴏʜɴ

F1 Hyjula
Mᴏʟᴇ; SʙS

Improved Hispi see Kingspi
Jersey Wakefield
Early pointed variety, forming small firm hearts. (Bree)
Bʀᴇᴇ; Jᴏʜɴ; SʙS; Tᴏᴢᴇ

Cabbage

June Giant see Golden Acre
June Star see Princess
F1 Kalorama
   JOHN

F1 King Greens
   RSLU

F1 Kingspi
   MARS

F1 Krautman
   BAKK

Langedijk 3 Starkwinter
   SBS; TOZE

Langedijk 4
The traditional white dutch cabbage for cutting October/November. Will keep for
weeks if stored in a ool, airy place. (Unwi)
   JOHN; MARS; SBS; TOZE; UNWI; VANH

Langedijk 4 Decema
Attractive drumhead for maturing late autumn. Very resistant to weather damage.
Can be cut as required over the early winter period. (Brwn)
   BRWN; MOLE; SBS

Langedijk Superstar
   SBS

Late Green Winter
   SBS

Late Winter Giant see Langedijk 4
Lincoln Imp
   SBS

F1 Marathon
   BREE

F1 Market Prize
   SBS

Marner Allfruh
Open pollinated variety with small, solid round heads covering a good cutting
period. Sow February-March, plant 18 in. apart, harvest July-August. (OGC)
   EWK; JOHN; OGC; SBS; YATE

Marner Rocco
   SBS

F1 Marquis Greens
RSLu

F1 Marvellon
T&M

F1 Metino
RSLu

F1 Metis
RSLu

F1 Mighty Globe
OGC; ROG; SBS; SMM

F1 Minicole
BRWN; CGAR; D&D; DOB; EWK; FOTH; JOHN; JWB; MOLE; OGC; ROG; SBS; SMM; SUFF; SUTT; T&M; TUCK; UNWI; VANH; WALL

F1 Multiton
JOHN

F1 Musketeer
BREE

Myatts Early Offenham
For quality dark green hearts. (JWB)
JWB

Noblesse
SBS

Offenham
Strong growing with large pointed heads for late April maturity. (EWK)
EWK; OGC; ROG; SBS; SMM; WALL

Offenham 1 Little Kempsey
SBS

Offenham 1 Myatts Offenham Compacta
A very uniform stock which is very early and dark green. (Bree)
BREE; BRWN; JOHN; MARS; MOLE; RSLu; SBS; TOZE; YATE

Offenham 2 First and Best
SBS

Offenham 2 Flower of Spring
For late eating (March onwards). Sow in September. Nice flavour. (D&D)
CGAR; CHIL; D&D; DOB; EWK; FOTH; JOHN; JWB; MOLE; OGC; ROG; SBS; SMM; SUTT; TOZE; TUCK; WALL

Cabbage

Offenham 3 Kempsey
SBS; YATE

Offenham BG 283
SBS

Offenham Compacta see Offenham 1 Myatts Offenham Compacta
Offenham Hardy Offenham
Bred to give a pointed dark green late variety for the second half of May. (Toze)
TOZE

F1 Oscar
FOTH

F1 Pedrillo
JOHN; SBS; TOZE

F1 Perfect Ball
T&M

Pewa
SBS; YATE

F1 Picolo
TOZE

F1 Pict
BREE

F1 Piton
BREE

Pixie
Very early. The compact plants produce very tight hearts and have few other leaves. Suitable for close spacing and ideal for small gardens. (Mars)
BRWN; DOB; MARS; SUTT; T&M; TOZE; UNWI

F1 Polestar
SBS

F1 Polinius
JOHN; MARS; SBS; TOZE

Primax
SBS

Primo see Golden Acre
F1 Prince Greens
RSLU

F1 Princess
SBS

F1 Prospera
BRWN; EWK; MOLE; SBS; WALL

F1 Puma
TOZE; YATE

F1 Quickstep
MARS; T&M

F1 Quisto
BREE

F1 Ramco
BREE

F1 Rapid
SBS

F1 Rapier
T&M

F1 Rinda
RSLU

Robinsons Champion
Large ox and cow cabbage for stock feed. (JWB)
CGAR; JOHN; JWB; MAS; ROB; SBS

F1 Rodeo
SBS

F1 Rodon
SBS

Roem van Enkhuizen see Enkhuizen Glory
F1 Sagitta
RSLU

F1 Scanvi
YATE

Scarisbrick
SBS

F1 Scimitar
SBS

F1 Slawdena
JOHN; SBS; TOZE

F1 Sparkel
DOB; FOTH

Cabbage

F1 Spartan
SBS

F1 Sphinx
RSLu

F1 Spirit
SBS

F1 Spitfire
DOB; FOTH; MOLE; OGC; SBS; TOZE; WALL

F1 Spivoy
FOTH

F1 Spring Hero
CGAR; D&D; DOB; EWK; FOTH; JOHN; JWB; MARS; MOLE; OGC; ROG; SBS;
SMM; TUCK; UNWI; WALL; YATE

Spring Time
SBS

Standby
Autumn ballhead. Stands well until wanted in September/October period without
bursting. (Toze)
SBS; TOZE

Starski
YATE

Steenkop see Stonehead

F1 Stetson
BREE

F1 Stonehead
BREE; BRWN; CGAR; DOB; EWK; FOTH; JOHN; JWB; MOLE; OGC; SBS; TOZE;
WALL; YATE

F1 Storan
SBS

Summer Monarch see Emerald Cross

F1 Supergreen
SBS

F1 Trevor
BREE

F1 Trumpet
BREE

Utility
JOHN

F1 Vanguard
MARS

F1 Vantage Point
SBS

Vienna see Green Wonder
Volga
MOLE

Wheelers Imperial
An old variety but still a fine early. Small pointed heads. (Dob)
BRWN; CART; CGAR; CHIL; DOB; EWK; JOHN; JWB; MOLE; ROG; SBS; SMM; SUTT; TUCK; WALL; YATE

Wiam
Very solid round heads. Matures in September and holds well. Especially sweet sort for use raw, in salads. (Mars)
MARS; MOLE; SBS; UNWI

F1 Winchester
BREE

Winnigstadt
An older, still very popular cabbage. Tightly wrapped leaves with hard, pointed hearts. (Dob)
CGAR; CHIL; D&D; DOB; EWK; FOTH; JOHN; JWB; MARS; MAS; MOLE; OGC; ROG; SBS; SUFF; SUTT; TUCK; VANH; WALL

Winnigstadter see Winnigstadt
Wintergreen see Offenham 3 Wintergreen
BREE; CGAR; EWK; JOHN; JWB; MARS; OGC; ROG; RSLU; SBS; SUFF; TOZE; TUCK; WALL; YATE

Wintergreen see Offenham 3 Wintergreen

Cabbage Abyssinian
Karate
CHAM

Cabbage Chinese Headed

Brassica rapa var. pekinensis
Chinese cabbage comes in two basic varieties, headed and loose-headed. Some are very susceptible to bolting, and it is important to choose appropriate varieties and sow at the correct time.

F1 Chiko
JOHN

Chin Suan
The green part of the plant, which can be cut all summer and autumn, has a distinctive aroma, suggestive of garlic and onion. Also called "garlic -chives". (Bakk)
BAKK

F1 China Express
EWK; SBS

F1 China King 14
CHIL

Early Jade Pagoda see Michihili
F1 Eskimo
SUFF

F1 Festival
JOHN

F1 Green Rocket
JOHN; SBS

F1 Harmony
SUTT; YATE

F1 Hopkin
BREE

F1 Hypro
RSLU

F1 Jade Pagoda
EWK; SUFF; TOZE; YATE

F1 Kasumi
JOHN; MARS; SBS; TOZE

F1 Kingdom
JOHN

F1 Mariko
T&M

Market Pride
An early variety with light green, savoyed outer leaves and pure white hearts. Produces cylindrical heads weighing about four pounds. (Chil)
CHIL

Michihili
SBS

F1 Monument
BAKK; JOHN

F1 Nagaoka
BRWN; SBS; TOZE

F1 Nagaoka 50 Days
MOLE

F1 Nagaoka 60 day
FOTH

F1 Nerva
BAKK

F1 Okido
SBS

F1 Orange Queen
SBS; SUFF; T&M

Pe-tsai
Not a variety name.
CGAR; CHIL; D&D; EWK; OGC; SBS; WALL

F1 Ruffles
DOB; SUTT

Santo
SBS

Santo Round Leaved
This is a non-heading variety giving plants with medium green, rounded leaves with white ribs. Cold resistant and easy to grow, it makes excellent eating. (Chil)
CHIL

Santo Serrated Leaved
Very hardy, this is an open leaved cabbage with decorative serrated leaves. Autumn/winter or spring vegetable. Excellent as a quick growing seedling crop to be cut when a few inches high. (Suff)
CHIL; SUFF

Shaho Tsai
SBS

Cabbage Chinese Headed

F1 Shanghai
SUFF

Shantung
Nice to look at, nice to eat, this is an early, semi-heading variety of spreading habit with light green leaves that are smooth and tender. Dense interior leaves that blanch well. Heads weigh about four or five pounds. (Chil)
CHIL

F1 Tako
YATE

F1 Tango
SBS; YATE

F1 Tip Top
JOHN; JWB; OGC; SBS; TUCK

F1 Tip Top 12
CHIL

F1 Tip Top China Express
BAKK; CGAR; TOZE

F1 Tonkin
BREE; SBS

Tsai Shim
The flowering stalks of Tsai Shim are delicious either fryed or boiled by themselves or with other vegetables or meat. They are picked immediately after flowering begins, six to eight weeks after sowing, leaving three or four young leaves on the plant. Successive stalks will them grow from the leaf axil, particularly if the plant is given a feed after each picking a continuing harvest can be enjoyed. Grows well from late spring to early autumn and is highly recommended for the ordinary, home gardener. (Chil)
CHIL

Tsoisam
SUFF

F1 WR 60 Days
SBS

Wong Bok see Pe-tsai

Cabbage Other

Couve Tronchuda

A splendid cabbage-like plant growing to 2 ft. or more across, with closely set leaves with thick, white, fleshy ribs forming a loose kind of head. The leaves and head are very tender to eat, and the midribs, said to have a distinct and agreeable flavour, cooked like Sea Kale. It withstands frost well - indeed it helps to develop the flavour - but it is probably best grown like a half-hardy annual. (Chil)

CHIL

Jersey Walking Stick

The long straight stems can be dried, producing attractive lightweight wood that makes into walking sticks. Mature height 5-7 ft. and if left for another season will reach 16 ft. The edible tops resemble kale. (Foth)

CHIL; FOTH; T&M

Cabbage Red

Brassica oleracea convar. capitata

F1 Autoro
JOHN; TOZE

F1 Hardoro
EWK; JOHN; OGC; SBS

F1 Kempero
JOHN

Landedijk Red Red King
Produces solid large heads with good red colour. We recommend this for cooking and pickling. Sow mid March, harvest July/August. Very long standing. (VanH)

VANH

Langedijk Red Autumn see Langedijk Red Medium
Langedijk Red Late
Excellent variety for storing that can be harvested from September. Sturdy plants with a weight of approx. 3.5kg. (Bakk)

BAKK; SBS

Langedijk Red Medium
An early deep red variety. (Dob)

DOB; JOHN

Langedijker Bewaar see Langedijk Red Late
Langedijker Herfst see Langedijk Red Medium
Niggerhead
SBS

F1 Normiro
John

F1 Rebus
Bree

Red Drumhead 2
A large globe cabbage for pickling, cooking and winter salads. Sow in July for winter. (D&D)
Bakk; Brwn; CGar; Chil; D&D; EWK; John; JWB; Mars; Mole; OGC; Rog; SMM; Sutt; T&M; Tuck; VanH; Wall

Red Dutch see Red Drumhead
Red King see Langedijk Red
Red Kissendrup
Later maturing than Meteor. Deep red colour. Sown in spring it keeps well in the autumn and early winter. (Toze)
Toze

Red Meteor
Sow early spring in frames or outdoors for late summer crops. (Toze)
Toze

F1 Redar
Bree

F1 Revue
Bree

F1 Rodima
Yate

F1 Rona
RSlu

Roodkop see Red Drumhead
F1 Rookie
Foth; SbS; Yate

F1 Roxy
RSlu

F1 Ruby Ball
Bakk; EWK; Foth; John; JWB; Mars; SbS; Suff; Unwi; Yate

F1 Ruby Perfection
Bakk

Volga
SbS

F1 Vorox
RSLU

Cabbage Savoy
F1 Alaska
BREE; SBS

Alexanders No 1
Uniform, solid heads mature in the New Year and hold longer than any other variety well into spring. (Mars)
JOHN; MARS

Alexanders No 1 Lincoln Late
SBS

F1 Aquarius
JOHN; JWB

Avon Coronet
SBS

Best Of All
Excellent garden variety producing firm flattish heads. (Tuck)
BRWN; CART; DOB; EWK; JOHN; JWB; MOLE; SBS; SUFF; TUCK; WALL

F1 Bingo
BRWN; JOHN; T&M

F1 Cantasa
JOHN

F1 Celsa
BAKK; JOHN

F1 Celtic
BRWN; CGAR; DOB; EWK; FOTH; JOHN; JWB; MARS; MOLE; OGC; ROG; SBS; SMM; SUTT; TOZE; TUCK; UNWI; VANH; WALL; YATE

F1 Chirimen
FOTH; SBS; YATE

F1 Concerto
YATE

F1 Corsair
DOB

De Pontoise 3 see January King

F1 Denver
BREE

F1 Hamasa
BAKK; SBS

Hammer Herba
MOLE

Herfstgroene see Novum

F1 Ice Queen
CGAR; D&D; EWK; SBS; SMM; TUCK; UNWI; VANH; WALL

F1 Icecap
BREE; SBS

January King
Excellent strain for Winter use. Solid heads with distinct colouring. Very hardy.
(EWK)
CGAR; CHIL; EWK; FOTH; JWB; MARS; OGC; ROG; SBS; SMM; SUFF; T&M;
UNWI; VANH; WALL

January King Hardy Late Stock 3
Very uniform stock selected over many years by an English breeder. It is extremely
hardy and will stand well into March and April. (Mars)
BREE; BRWN; CART; DOB; JOHN; MARS; MOLE; RSLU; SBS; SUTT; TOZE; TUCK;
WALL; YATE

January King Improved Extra Late
SBS

January King Improved Late
SBS

F1 Julius
BREE; JOHN; T&M; TOZE

Late Drumhead
A very popular old variety that is ready for cutting February/March from a May/
June sowing. (Suff)
JWB; SBS; SUFF

F1 Lucetta
JOHN

F1 Marabel
JOHN; SBS; T&M; TOZE

Marner Lagerweiss
SBS

F1 Mila
BREE; SBS

F1 Morgan
BRWN; JOHN

Novum
SBS

F1 Novusa
JOHN; MARS; TOZE

Ormskirk
Large variety, good frost resistance. (D&D)
D&D; EWK; OGC; VANH

Ormskirk see Late Drumhead

Ormskirk (I)
A very hardy grey-green crinkled leaved savoy maturing December to January and standing for a long time. (Unwi)
UNWI

Ormskirk (I) Ormskirk Late
Hearts in January/March, very hardy and solid with lovely flavour. (Mars)
BRWN; CHIL; DOB; JOHN; JOHN; MARS; SBS; WALL

Ormskirk (I) Rearguard
SUTT

Ormskirk Early
SBS

Ormskirk Extra Late
True Savoy type with dark green crimpled foliage. Will cut even into April. (Tuck)
MOLE; SBS; TUCK

Ormskirk Medium
SBS

F1 Ovasa
JOHN

F1 Paresa
JOHN; TOZE

Perfection Drumhead
EWK; SBS; WALL

F1 Prelude
YATE

Cabbage Savoy

F1 Protovoy
DOB

F1 Rhapsody
YATE

F1 Saga
RSLU

F1 Salarite
BAKK

Savoy King
Unsurpassed for yield, uniformity and vigour, it has solid heads of superb flavour. (Foth)
EWK; FOTH; T&M; T&M; UNWI

F1 Silva
SUTT

F1 Sindria
RSLU

Starski
A vigorous variety producing good solid heads which store well. Some frost resistance and it retains its colour through the Winter. (OGC)
CGAR; EWK; OGC; SBS; TUCK

F1 Stilon
RSLU

F1 Taler
MARS; RSLU

F1 Tarvoy
EWK; JOHN; SBS; T&M

F1 Tasmania
BREE; BRWN; SBS

F1 Tombola
SBS

F1 Tundra
BRWN; DOB; JOHN; MARS; MOLE; OGC; SBS; T&M; TOZE; YATE

Vertus
Well developing autumn cabbage giving a high yield of tight cabbages. Beautiful, dark green variety with lightly crimped leaves. (Bakk)
BAKK

Winter King
Excellent cabbage with a good flavour, suitable to remain in the field for a long time, as well as for prolonged refrigerated storing. (Bakk)
BAKK; MARS; SBS; TOZE; VANH

Winter King Harda
An outstanding variety with good frost resistance for cutting December to March. (Suff)
MOLE; SBS; SUFF

Winter King Shortie
SBS

F1 Winter Star
SBS

F1 Winterton
BRWN; JOHN; SUTT; TOZE

F1 Wintessa
EWK; JOHN; SBS; TOZE

F1 Wirosa
BRWN; JOHN; JWB; MOLE; TOZE; TUCK; VANH; YATE

F1 Wivoy
DOB; JOHN; MARS; SBS; TOZE

F1 Yslanda
JOHN

Camas

Camassia quamash
An edible bulb native to North Western USA and a favourite of the native tribes of the are. The plants grow to nearly 1 m. and have narrow strap-like leaves. The tall flowering spike consists of many striking blue-violet flowers 2.5 cm. long and very ornamental. After the plant has died down the bulbs can be harvested. They are 3-5 cm. across and are eaten baked, roasted or boiled and have a flavour similar to chestnuts. (Futu)

Camas
Sent in autumn. (Futu)
FUTU

Cape Gooseberry
Physalis peruviana and others
Related to tomatoes, the deliciously aromatic edible fruits are enclosed in papery lanterns.
Plants can sprawl, so allow plenty of space.

Bladder Cherry
CHIL

Cape Gooseberry
Half hardy annual with spreading shoots, the pale green "lantern" flowers contain edible round yellow fruits. Grows in greenhouse or sheltered border. (OGC)
DOB; OGC; SMM; SUFF; SUTT

Cossack Pineapple
A low, trailing annual similar to the tomatillo, with small fruits, about 2 cm. across, enclosed by husks that turn tan coloured when ripe. The fruits are sweeter than those of the tomatillo and can be eaten raw or made into excellent jam. (Futu)
FUTU

Golden Berry
Producing orange berries up to 1 in. across which are a tangy sweet mixture of pineapple and strawberry. Each fruit is enclosed in a papery Chinese lantern-like casing. Grow like bush tomatoes. Will crop outdoors in South in a sunny sheltered site, otherwise best in a cool greenhouse. (T&M)
FOTH; T&M; UNWI

Pineapple Cherry
BAKK

Cardoon
Cynara cardunculus
Very similar to artichokes, but it is the blanched stems, rather than the flowers, that are eaten.

Cardoon
Related to the Globe Artichoke but grown for its blanched stems. Use as an alternative to fennel or celery. (OGC)
CGAR; CHAM; CHIL; EWK; JWB; OGC; SBS; SMM

Gigante di Romagna
A marvellous decorative architectural plant for the vegetable or flower garden. Tie up the long stalks to blanche the inner heart like celery. Harvest December. Needs lots of space. (Suff)
SUFF

Carrot

Daucus carota

F1 Almaro
RSLU; T&M

Amsterdam Bak see Amsterdam Forcing 3

Amsterdam Forcing see Amsterdam Forcing 3

Amsterdam Forcing
ROG

Amsterdam Forcing 3
Early carrot, extremely suitable for sowing early in a cold frame. Good for cultivation in the open. (Bakk)
BAKK; CGAR; D&D; DOB; EWK; FOTH; JOHN; JWB; MARS; MOLE; OGC; SBS; SUTT; TOZE; TUCK; WALL

Amsterdam Forcing Caramba
BREE

Amsterdam Outdoor see Amsterdam Forcing 3

Amsterdam Sweetheart
This is the variety to grow if you love the flavour of young "Finger Carrots"! Pull them as young as possible, and enjoy their superb sweet flavour. Splendid for freezing - so none need be wasted. (Unwi)
UNWI

F1 Anglia
BREE; WALL

Astra
Nantaise type medium early variety. Length 15-17cms. Good resistance to splitting and breaking. For main crop and overwintering. (EWK)
EWK

Autumn King
A true winter carrot: robust vegetable, producing a heavy carrot which is, however, fairly smooth. It has a beautiful colour inside and outside. (Bakk)
BAKK; CGAR; CHIL; D&D; EWK; FOTH; JOHN; JWB; MAS; MOLE; OGC; ROG; SBS; SMM; SUTT; WALL

Autumn King 2
Long large roots. Fine deep rich red internal colour. Can be left in the ground for winter without splitting. Reliable heavy yielding main crop for eating fresh, winter storage or freezing, cropping late summer to autumn. (T&M)
CART; DOB; T&M

Carrot

Autumn King 2 Vita Longa
A long stump-rooted variety. Heavy cropping, mostly red cored, and excellent keeper. Late harvesting type. (Brwn)
    BRWN; EWK; JOHN; MARS; SBS; SUFF; TUCK; UNWI

Autumn King Red Winter
    SBS

Autumn King Trophy
    BREE

Autumn King Viking
    SBS

F1 Bangor
    SUTT

Banta
Sturdy, well coloured roots with high carotene content. Heavy top for good protection and easy lifting. (EWK)
    SBS

Beacon
A British bred maincrop variety producing uniform long slightly tapered roots. Gives a heavy yield and in trials has gained top ratings for both flesh and core colour. Flavour first-class. (Sutt)
    SUTT

Bercoro
    RSLU

F1 Bergen
    JOHN

Berlicum
Beautiful, cylindrical, stump-rooted, red winter carrot. Narrow core. Fine flavour. (Bakk)
    BAKK; EWK; JOHN; SBS

Berlicum 2 Berjo
A late maincrop with outstanding colour and especially high in vitamin A. Cylindrical shape. (Suff)
    JOHN; MARS; MOLE; SBS; SUFF; TOZE

Berlicum 2 Oranza
Maincrop tupe of good core and flesh colour. Roots are almost cylindrical and of very high quality. Suitable for harvest from August to Christmas. Mid season. (Brwn)
    BRWN; SBS

Carrot

Berlicum 2 Zino
Has appeared in the Guiness Book of Records as the world's largest carrot. Huge well shaped roots with exceptionally high juice yield. Very large main crop. Excellent quality fresh, stored or juice. Cropping late summer and autumn. (T&M)
T&M

Berlicum Special
SBS

F1 Berlina
SBS; YATE

F1 Bernova
BAKK; SBS

F1 Bertan
T&M

F1 Bingo
YATE

F1 Boston
JOHN

Bridge
SBS

F1 Butor
TOZE

Camberley
A high quality half-long maincrop. Tapered roots are usually 7-9in. (17-23cm) long with a deep orange colour and a smooth skin. Used for overwintering, particularly in heavy soils, and recommended for both commercial and garden use. (OGC)
OGC

Campestra
An exceptionally good Autumn King type of appetising deep orange-red. The roots from 6-8in. long, are strong shouldered, slightly tapered and cylindrical. For use during autumn and early winter. (Dob)
CGAR; SBS

Camus
DOB

F1 Cardinal
DOB

F1 Carousel
JOHN

Carrot

Chanson
RSLU

Chantenay Babycan
Ideal for the production of baby carrots. Seed may be broadcast to provide up to 45 plants per square foot. Develops fast. Rich coloured with little core and great flavour. (Suff)
SUFF

F1 Chantenay Canners Favourite
YATE

F1 Chantenay Long
YATE

Chantenay Model Red Cored see Chantenay Red Cored
Chantenay Red Cored
A stump-rooted, early maincrop with small cored orange roots of fine texture. (Dob)
BREE; CART; CGAR; CHIL; D&D; DOB; EWK; JOHN; JWB; MAS; MOLE; OGC; ROG; SBS; SMM; TOZE; VANH; WALL

Chantenay Red Cored 2
A very good carrot, early, with thick, blunt ended roots. Suitable for early and late sowings. Stores well. (Unwi)
MARS; UNWI

Chantenay Red Cored 3 Supreme
A greatly improved stump rooted form, slightly larger with very smooth skin and a much better colour than the original, without losing any of its reliability. Early maincrop. Fresh eating, canning, freezing and winter storage. Exhibition. Repeat sowings spring/late summer. (T&M)
SBS; T&M

Chantenay Red Cored Fenman
SBS

Chantenay a Coeur Rouge see Chantenay Red Cored
Chantenay royal
A stump rooted main crop variety excellent in any soil, ideal for clay. Rich coloured roots. Fine flavour. (Suff)
BREE; EWK; JOHN; ROG; SBS; SUFF; TUCK

Chantenay royal 2
A high quality selected stump rooted variety. Mid season. (Brwn)
BRWN

Chantenay royal 2 Gold King
SBS

F1 Cobba
DOB; YATE

F1 Condor
BREE

F1 Coronet
SBS

D'Amsterdam a Forcer see Amsterdam Forcing 3
F1 Dakota
SBS

Danvers 126
SBS

Danvers Scarlet Intermediate
SBS

De Colmar a Coeur Rouge see Autumn King
Decora
Fast growing Nantes type with very smooth, heavy yielding roots. (EWK)
EWK; SBS

F1 Disco
YATE

F1 Dragon
TOZE

Duke
SBS

Early French Frame
Quick-maturing round roots up to 50mm (about 2 in) in diameter. Ideal for forcing or for sowing in succession outdoors. (Sutt)
JWB; SBS; SUTT

Early French Frame 4 Lisa
A big improvement on Rondo, it produces much rounder carrots without the deep cavity in the shoulder which is typical of other round carrots. (Mars)
MARS

Early Horn
For early use this medium sized short, stump rooted carrot is very reliable. RHS highly recommended. (Unwi)
FOTH; JOHN; JWB; SBS; UNWI

Carrot

Early Market
An early, stump-rooted variety of excellent quality, ideal for both early and late sowing. (John)
D&D; EWK; Rog; Tuck; Wall

Early Market Horn see Chantenay Red Cored
Early Nantes see Nantes
Early Scarlet Horn see Early Horn
Fakkell Mix
SBS

Fancy
SBS

F1 Favor
Toze

Favourite
One of the most popular stump-rooted maincrop varieties. Excellent quality and recommended for exhibition in "short" classes. (Sutt)
Sutt

F1 Fedora
One of the most productive late varieties we offer. The heavy, smooth-skinned roots are very large and conical with an excellent colour throughout. (Unwi)
SBS; Unwi

Fincor
RSlu

First Pull see Amsterdam Forcing 3
F1 Flacino
RSlu

Flak
Fly resistant. The most productive carrot suitable for practically any soils, for an early crop, sow during June/early July for harvesting October until March. An absolute cert for the show bench. Guiness Book of Record Holder 10lbs.4oz. (VanH)
CGar; VanH

Flakkee
Maincrop variety, large roots, excellent for the show bench. (JWB)
JWB

F1 Flashlight
SBS

F1 Flex
Bakk

F1 Fly Away
T&M

Foxey
SBS

Giganta
SMM

F1 Gregory
BREE; T&M; WALL

F1 Gringo
YATE

Guerande
A very old variety, with broad shoulders, stump rooted and early with a fine flavour. (Suff)
SBS; SUFF

Imperator
SBS

F1 Ingot
EWK; FOTH; SBS; T&M; TUCK; UNWI

F1 Ivor
TOZE

James Scarlet Intermediate
A good early maincrop variety, with symmetrical and well tapered roots. It is well coloured and is of a good texture, making it an ideal carrot for culinary purposes. (John)
CGAR; CHIL; D&D; EWK; FOTH; JOHN; JWB; OGC; ROG; SBS; TUCK; UNWI; VANH; WALL

F1 Jasper
DOB

Juared
A medium-early to medium-late variety, so it is not a true winter carrot. Juared is sometimes called the "health carrot", as it has the highest carotene content. Extremely rich in vitamin A. (Bakk)
BAKK; JOHN; SUFF; T&M

Jumbo
The variety not only holds the record for the longest carrot ever, but has also produced one of the heaviest carrots known. High yields of enormous roots for shows, competitions, etc. Cropping autumn to early winter. (T&M)
T&M

Carrot

Juwarot see Juared

Karotan
Long, stump-ended roots of large size for maincrop use. Excellent flavour with high juice content. (RSlu)
SBS; WALL

Kundulus
Window boxes, difficult soils, frames, small gardens. Very fast growing. (T&M)
CART; T&M

F1 Laranda
T&M

Laros
SBS

F1 Liberno
RSLU; T&M

Lobbericher
A sweet, yellow fodder carrot for cattle and rabbits, goats etc. Can be stored in a pit. (Bakk)
BAKK

Long Red Surrey see St Valery

F1 Lynx
BREE

F1 Major
TOZE

Minicor
Excellent flavour and colours up early. Uniform 6-7 in. Very slender roots. Best for "baby carrots". A gourmet variety. (Suff)
RSLU; SUFF

F1 Mokum
BAKK; CART; JOHN; T&M; VANH

F1 Nabora
YATE

F1 Nairobi
BRWN; JOHN

F1 Nanco
JOHN; JWB

F1 Nandor
CGAR; ROB; TOZE

Nantaise 2 Michel
SBS

Nantes
Half-long, stump ended roots. Strong grower of first class quality and flavour. (EWK)
CGAR; D&D; EWK; FOTH; JOHN; JWB; MAS; MOLE; SMM; SUFF; TUCK; VANH; ROG; WALL

Nantes 2
Very early and deservedly popular, long stump rooted with little core. (Unwi)
MARS; UNWI

Nantes 2 Ideal
DOB; SBS; SBS

Nantes 2 Romosa
A half long stump rooted early, excellent for forcing or outside sowing. Has very little core. A really succulent variety. First early. (Brwn)
BRWN

Nantes 5
CART; SUTT

Nantes 5 Champion Scarlet Horn
A fast maturing carrot of uniform shape and quality. (Dob)
DOB; SUTT

Nantes Express
Early maincrop. Suitable for early sowing in frames. Some cavity spot resistance. (T&M)
T&M; UNWI

Nantes Fruhbund
It colours very early and is, therefore, suitable for sowing early. A carrot with a good colour in- and outside, and with a very agreeable flavour. Recommended selection from the well-known Nantes group. (Bakk)
BAKK

Nantes Half Long
A well-known variety, popular for its high yields and its agreeable, sweet flavour. Nantes is a real summer carrot! (Bakk)
BAKK

F1 Nantes Nanthya
BREE

F1 Nantucket
JOHN

Carrot

Naomi
SBS

F1 Napoli
JOHN

F1 Narante
Uniformly cylindrical, stump-ended roots about 6in long and 1-1 1/2 in thick. The orange-red flesh is usually coreless and of sweet flavour. Useful both for early pulling or as a maincrop. (Dob)
BAKK

F1 Narbonne
JOHN

F1 Narman
JOHN; MOLE; SBS; VANH

F1 Narova
TUCK

F1 Navarre
FOTH; JOHN

F1 Nelson
JOHN; SUTT

New Radiance
SBS

New Red Intermediate see St Valery
F1 Newmarket
FOTH

Norfolk Giant see Autumn King
Obtuse de Doubs
A traditional French carrot which forms good-sized half long pointed carrots of an orange-yellow colour. Hardy with excellent eatring qualities. Rare. (Suff)
SUFF

F1 Panther
An exceptional carrot for the home gardener, this is an early hybrid of Nantes for summer cropping. The attractive orange red roots are up to 20cms/8ins long with short foliage and fine internal colouring. Resistance to cracking is also good and flavour is excellent. (Unwi)
BREE; UNWI

Parabell
SBS

Parisje Markt see Early French Frame
Parmex
A unique round carrot, 1-1.5 in. in diameter. Matures extra early and develops flavour and bright colour while still young. Perfect for growing in heavy soil. Superb with fresh green peas. (Suff)
> DOB; FOTH; JOHN; SUFF

F1 Presto
> JOHN

F1 Primo
> MARS

F1 Punta
> YATE

F1 Rapier
> TOZE

F1 Red Baron
> SBS

Red Chantenay
Very popular, excellent quality, good flavour. (JWB)
> JWB

Red Intermediate Stump Rooted
> CGAR; EWK; ROG

Red Intermediate Stump Rooted see Chantenay Red Cored
F1 Red Rum
> FOTH; SBS

Redca
A recent Chantenay introduction, stump rooted and very uniform. Excellent root colour with a nice smooth skin. (OGC)
> OGC

F1 Redco
> YATE

Regulus
> SBS

Rocket
> DOB; TOZE

Romosa
> SBS

Rondo
Produces almost round shaped roots. Very early, uniform and sweet tasting. Easy to clean and cook whole. (EWK)
CGAR; EWK; OGC; ROG; WALL

Rubin
An early, round carrot with a good inside colour and narrow core, contrary to most other ball-shaped carrots. A variety for the professional as well as for the amateur vegetable grower. (Bakk)
BAKK; SBS

Rusty
SBS

Saint-Valery see St Valery
Scarlet Nantes
SBS

F1 Sheila
YATE

St Valery
A pre 1880 variety from France with sweet tender flesh. For best results grow this carrot in a rich deep soil where it can attain a size of 2-3 in x 12 in! (Suff)
CGAR; CHIL; DOB; EWK; FOTH; JOHN; JWB; MARS; OGC; ROG; SBS; SMM; SUFF; SUTT; TUCK; VANH; WALL

St Valery Special Selection
Long tapered roots, very uniform and good colour. (Rob)
ROB

Suko
One of the earliest sweetest little carrots we know. Recommended where space is limited also shallow or heavy soils. (T&M)
JOHN; T&M

Sytan
This Nantes type carrot is less susceptible to carrot fly maggot than other varieties. (Mars)
MARS

F1 Tam-tam
YATE

F1 Tamino
CGAR; D&D; EWK; JOHN; OGC; ROG; SBS

F1 Tancar
TOZE

F1 Tardia
BREE

Tip Top
Nantes type, very good colour and quality. (JWB)
BREE; DOB; JWB; OGC; SBS; VANH

Top Score
SBS

Touchon
A well-known variety which remotely resembles Nantes. Excellent flavour and good colour. Just like Nantes a true summer carrot. (Bakk)
BAKK

Touchon Ideal Red
An old French variety (pre 1880) with a fine texture and superb flavour at any size. Will grow to 8 ins (20 cms). The best juicy carrot. Special improved selection. Main crop. (Suff)
SUFF; TOZE

F1 Turbo
YATE

Waltham Hicolour
SBS

White Fodder
Don't be put off by the name. A superb mild tasting carrot very much appreciated in France. Very easy to grow and remains deliciously tender even when very large. This is a safe carrot to eat for those allergic to carotene. (Suff)
OGC; SUFF

Cauliflower

Brassica oleracea convar. botrytis Alef. var. botrytis

AG 63
SBS

F1 AY 575
YATE

Ace Early
DOB; SBS

Ace High
SBS

Adams Early White
SBS

Cauliflower

Alban
YATE

Alice Springs
SBS

All Seasons see All The Year Round
All The Year Round
Can be sown in late autumn or spring to produce reliable, large, white heads from late June to October. (Foth)
BRWN; CART; CGAR; CHIL; D&D; DOB; EWK; FOTH; JOHN; JWB; MARS; MOLE; OGC; ROG; SBS; SMM; SUFF; SUTT; T&M; UNWI; VANH; WALL; YATE

Alpha
Very popular for early work, June/July. (JWB)
JWB

Alpha 5
Sow outside in early April for August cutting. Sow under glass September/January to mature June/July. It is a very good doer. (Mars)
MARS; SUTT

Alpha Ajubro
SBS

Alpha Begum
JOHN

Alpha Fortados
RSLU

Alpha Jubro
JOHN

Alverda
Excellent quality yellow-green curds with good flavour makes a nice change to the usual white varieties. Sow late May/June for autumn cropping. (OGC)
BAKK; JOHN; OGC; SUFF

Angers Early see Angers No 2
Angers Extra Early see Angers No 1
Angers Extra Late see Angers No 5
Angers Half Early see Angers No 3
Angers Late see Angers No 4
Angers No 1
Specially recommended for Southern and Western regions. Unsuitable for cold or exposed areas. All have pure white, solid curds. Heads January-February. (Sutt)
SBS; SUTT

Cauliflower

Angers No 2 see Angers No. 1. Matures February-March. (Sutt)
  MARS; SBS; SUTT; UNWI

Angers No 3
  SBS

Angers No 4
  SBS

Angers No 5
  SBS

Aprilex
  BREE; JOHN; SBS; YATE

F1 Arbon
  JOHN; RSLU; TOZE

F1 Arcade
  RSLU

F1 Arfak
  RSLU

Armado
  RSLU

Armel 2
We can confidently recommend this variety for any part of the United Kingdom.
Truly exceptional curds and above all robust and reliable. (T&M)
  YATE

F1 Armetta
  BAKK; RSLU

Arminda
  JOHN; MOLE; SBS

F1 Arven
  BREE; WALL

Asmer Bostonian see Walcheren Winter 5

Asmer Juno
Usually cuts into June, producing large heads of superb quality before the first early
summer cauliflowers are ready. (Mars)
  MARS

Asmer Snowcap March
The earliest variety of the hardy English type. (Mars)
  MARS

Cauliflower

F1 Aston Purple
  YATE

Aubade
The compact, smooth, solid curd has excellent flavour, cooks beautifully and holds its colour. (Foth)
  FOTH

Autumn Giant
Large heads for cutting from October onwards. (EWK)
  CHIL; EWK; JOHN; JWB; MOLE; ROG; SBS; VANH; WALL

Autumn Giant 3
Beautiful white firm heads, thoroughly protected by the leaves. Excellent for cutting in November and December. (T&M)
  CGAR; SBS; T&M

Autumn Giant 4
  DOB; SUTT

Autumn Glory
An old favourite but still deservedly popular. Exceedingly large heads of the finest quality. (Unwi)
  UNWI

F1 Aviso
  JOHN; TOZE

F1 Baco
  JOHN; RSLU; TOZE

F1 Balmoral
  YATE

F1 Bambi
  BREE; SBS

Barrier Reef
Compact habit, well-protected deep, white, solid curds. Matures late October. (Sutt)
  BRWN; CGAR; CHIL; D&D; EWK; JOHN; JWB; MARS; MOLE; ROG; SBS; SUFF; SUTT; TUCK; VANH; WALL; YATE

Batsman
A very vigorous variety which produces excellent quality white curds which are well protected. (Foth)
  FOTH; JOHN; TOZE

F1 Bergen
  BREE

Boston Prize Early
SbS

Briac 30
Australian type with large heads and short growing habit. Sow mid-May for maturity to mid-November. (EWK)
Toze; Yate

F1 Briten
Bree; Wall

F1 Calan
John; Toze

Cambridge Early Giant
SbS

Cambridge Mid Giant
SbS

Canberra
Australian variety for November cutting. Large solid heads of excellent colour and quality. (EWK)
CGar; Mars; Rog; SMM

F1 Candid Charm
EWK; OGC; Rog; SbS; Suff; Tuck; VanH; Yate

Cargill
Specially chosen for mini-cauliflower use it is quick growing, vigorous and without a heavy foliage canopy and will not mature all at once. (T&M)
John; T&M; Yate

F1 Carlos
John; RSlu; Toze

F1 Castlegrant
Yate

F1 Ciren
Bree

F1 Commander
Bree

Corvilia
Large head size, rather smooth and slightly domed in shape. Late summer to late autumn. (EWK)
SbS; Yate

Cauliflower

Decidura
A superb quality with heavy curds and a long maturing phase making it suitable for harvest in the difficult autumn to early winter period. Displays good tolerance to cold, providing the last of the seasons harvest before the winter types mature. (Foth)
FOTH

Dok Elgon
Matures about 13 weeks after planting. Excellent as an early and late autumn crop. Vigorous growing with well-covered, firm, round, snow-white heads. (Mars)
BRWN; CGAR; D&D; DOB; EWK; FOTH; JOHN; JWB; MARS; MOLE; OGC; ROB; ROG; RSLU; SBS; SMM; SUTT; T&M; TUCK; UNWI; VANH; WALL

Dominant
Grows well in dry conditions with strong broad foliage for good protection. Autumn heading. (EWK)
BRWN; EWK; JOHN; MARS; MOLE; OGC; SBS; WALL

F1 Dova
BRWN; JOHN; RSLU; SBS; TOZE

Dutch May Heading 0581 see Walcheren Winter 5
Early Feltham see Angers No 2
Early Snowball
JOHN

F1 Elby
DOB; RSLU; SBS; T&M; TOZE

English Winter
SBS

Erfurt Prima see Snowball
Ewk's Late June
Heading during June. (JWB)
EWK; JWB; SBS

Ewk's May Star
Heading during May. (JWB)
JWB

Extra Early Feltham see Angers No 1
Extra Late Feltham see Angers No 5
F1 Fargo
JOHN; T&M

Firstman
JOHN

Fleurly
An excellent addition! Fleurly produces solid clear white heads of exceptionally high quality. Cut from mid-late April from a late-May sowing. (Dob)
DOB; MOLE; SBS

Flora Blanca
Matures September and October. Deep, pure white heads of first-class quality. Excellent for exhibition. (Sutt)
SUTT

Florian 51
Exceptional solid white heads and a strong weather resistance. (Foth)
TOZE; YATE

Fortuna
MOLE; SBS

F1 Fremont
RSLU

Garant
Quick growing mini cauliflower. (EWK)
EWK; OGC; SMM; SUFF

Grandessa
Medium large heads of pure white for autumn cutting. Strong mid green foliage giving excellent protection. (EWK)
BAKK

Grodan
JOHN; MOLE; SBS; WALL

F1 Hawkesbury
YATE

Herfstreuzen see Autumn Giant
Idol
DOB

Inca
April heading variety with excellent white heads. Strong leaf protection and very frost resistant. (EWK)
CGAR; EWK; JOHN; OGC; ROG; SBS; SUFF; TOZE; WALL

Jaudy 45
TOZE; YATE

F1 Jerome
JOHN; MARS

Cauliflower

Juno
Winter heading, excellent quality, sow April to June matures following May/June. (JWB)
   JWB

Kangeroo
   SBS

Kestral
   SBS

King
Medium large heads of pure white for autumn cutting. Strong mid green foliage giving excellent protection. (EWK)
   EWK; MOLE; ROG; SBS; WALL; YATE

Late Adonis see Walcheren Winter 7
Late Feltham see Angers No 4
Late Queen
   SBS

Lateman
A versatile, medium sized variety with lovely deep white curds. Sow from March to May for cutting August to October. (Dob)
   BRWN; DOB; JOHN; VANH

Lawnya
   SBS

Leamington
   SBS

Lecerf
A fool-proof cropper of excellent quality, having large, deep white heads with dark green upright leaves. For summer use sow March/April; for autumn use May/June. (VanH)
   VANH

Lenton Monarch
   SBS

Limelight
A beautiful soft green autumn cauliflower which retains its colour after cooking. Easy from a May sowing. (Mars)
   MARS

Lincoln Early
   SBS

F1 Linday
BREE

F1 Lindon
BREE

F1 Lindurian
BREE

F1 Linero
BREE

F1 Linex
BREE

F1 Linford
BREE

F1 Linmont
BREE

F1 Lintop
BREE

F1 Logan
JOHN

Macerata
TOZE

Majestic see Autumn Giant 3
Markanta
Extra high quality, with pure white, deep curds produced from early May onwards. (Mars)
FOTH; JWB; MARS

F1 Marmalade
DOB; YATE

F1 Martian
SBS

May Blossom
SBS

Maya
Late May heading. Very hardy, produces well protected, high quality curds. Can be sown as late as June. (Tuck)
CGAR; D&D; EWK; OGC; ROG; SBS; TUCK; VANH; WALL

Mechelse Carillon
BREE; SBS

Cauliflower

Mechelse Lincoln Early see Lincoln Early
Midsummer
    SᴮS

Minaret
Lime green small pointed florets of excellent flavour for late autumn cropping.
(Brwn)
    Bʀwɴ; Jᴏʜɴ; Mᴏʟᴇ

F1 Montano
    Bʀᴇᴇ; Mᴀʀs

F1 Nautilus
    Bʀwɴ; Jᴏʜɴ; Tᴏᴢᴇ

Nevada
    SᴮS

New Late Dutch see Walcheren Winter 6
Oze
    SᴮS

Pacific Charm
    SᴮS

F1 Pamir
    RSʟu

Panda
Mechelse type for early summer production. Perfectly round snow-white heads that
withstand high temperatures very well. (EWK)
    D&D; EWK; SᴮS; Tucк

Perfection
A very reliable variety for October or January sowings. (Brwn)
    Bʀwɴ; EWK; Jᴏʜɴ; Mᴏʟᴇ; SᴮS; SMM; Tᴏᴢᴇ; Wᴀʟʟ; Yᴀᴛᴇ

F1 Plana
    Mᴀʀs; RSʟu; T&M

Polaris see Alpha
F1 Predil
    Mᴏʟᴇ; RSʟu; Wᴀʟʟ

Predominant
An easy to grow, mini-cauliflower, can be sown later for heads maturing in September/October. (T&M)
    Tᴏᴢᴇ

Primel No 25
TOZE

F1 Profil
MOLE; WALL

Purdy
SBS

Purple Cape
A hardy purple cauliflower cropping in February and March. The curd turns green when cooked and has a fine flavour. (Mars)
BREE; CHIL; DOB; JOHN; JWB; MARS; MOLE; OGC; SBS; SUFF; T&M; TOZE; UNWI; WALL; YATE

Purple Oak
SBS

Purple Queen
Vigorous grower and very uniform. Deep purple heads for early autumn maturity. (EWK)
CGAR; EWK; ROG; VANH

Revito
BAKK; JOHN; SBS; TOZE; YATE

Rosalind
A quick growing purple headed variety for autumn cutting. Sow late May and June. Well worth trying. (Suff)
CART; SUFF; TOZE

Royal Oak
Very fine late variety, heads in May. (Barb)
SBS

F1 Sergeant
BREE

Sernio
RSLU

F1 Serrano
BREE

Sierra
A strong growing variety and good covering ability. Maturing late summer to early autumn. (Brwn)
BRWN; RSLU

F1 Siria
JOHN

Cauliflower

Snow Cap see Snowcap

Snow Crown
Sow May/June, January cutting. (Barb)
JWB; MARS; SBS; UNWI

F1 Snow February
SBS

F1 Snow Flake
BAKK

F1 Snow King
SBS

F1 Snow Prince
EWK; SBS

Snow White
Specially recommended for southern and western regions. Unsuitable for cold or exposed areas. Pure white solid curds, for use March-April. (Sutt)
SUTT

Snow's Winter White
Invaluable and popular mid-winter cauliflower. Cold tolerant and easier to grow than spring varieties. (T&M)
SBS; T&M

Snowball
Compact and very early with solid pure white heads of superb quality. Can be sown as early as January and also during autumn. (Dob)
CART; CGAR; DOB; EWK; FOTH; JWB; MOLE; ROG; SBS; SMM; SUFF; SUTT; VANH; WALL

F1 Snowbred
This is a greatly improved type from the original, and is a first class early market variety, we continue to offer it because of the demand. (Brwn)
CHIL; EWK; OGC; SBS; TUCK

Snowcap
Very late variety that can be cut over a long period. Ready in 22 weeks from an early June sowing. (EWK)
CGAR; D&D; EWK; JWB; MOLE; OGC; ROG; SBS; TUCK; WALL; YATE

Snowy River
SBS

Solide
MOLE; WALL

St George
A later variety, ready for harvesting in April and May, giving solid pure white heads. (John)
JOHN; SBS

St Mark
SBS

F1 Stella
JOHN; TOZE

Swan Lake
SBS

Tavia
YATE

F1 Taymount
YATE

Thanet see Walcheren Winter 3
Triskel 22
Produces superb quality heads in the hotter months of the year when other varieties are often poor. Sow April to mature late August; early May for September. (Mars)
TOZE; YATE

F1 Tulchan
SUTT; YATE

Valentine
SBS

Veitch's Autumn Giant Early
JOHN

Veitch's Self Protecting
Strong growing, late autumn heading. Will stand into November without spoiling. (EWK)
CGAR; D&D; EWK; JOHN; ROG; SBS; WALL

Vernon
MOLE; SBS

Vilna
The latest maturing overwinter cauliflower. Maturing end of May to mid-June. Very hardy. (Brwn)
BRWN; CGAR; JOHN; TOZE

F1 Violet Queen
BREE; JOHN; OGC; SBS; SUTT; WALL; YATE

Cauliflower

Vision
A sister variety to Vilna, with the same characteristics. Slightly earlier maturing, mid-end of May. (Brwn)
BRWN; JOHN; TOZE

Walcheren Winter
This excellent variety produces tasty, wide heads from April until June. (Tuck)
DOB

Walcheren Winter 1 Armado April
Superb-quality extra white curds maturing mid-April onwards. An outstanding variety. (Mars)
BRWN; CGAR; D&D; JOHN; JWB; MARS; MOLE; OGC; ROG; RSLU; SBS; T&M; TOZE; TUCK; VANH; WALL

Walcheren Winter 2 Armado May
Recommded for any part of the UK. Exceptional curds and above all robust and reliable. (T&M)
JOHN; MOLE; RSLU; SBS; T&M; TOZE

Walcheren Winter 3
SUTT

Walcheren Winter 3 Armado April
Superb quality heads of pure white and large size. Cutting late April. (EWK)
EWK

Walcheren Winter 3 Armado Tardo
Solid, crunchy, pure white curds that will provide you with garden-fresh florets in one of the few periods in the year when, until now, it wasn't so easy to find a good late spring/early summer variety. Crops late April/early May. (Unwi)
JOHN; MOLE; RSLU; SBS; TOZE; UNWI

Walcheren Winter 3 Marchpast
BREE; SBS

Walcheren Winter 5
SBS

Walcheren Winter 5 May
OGC; TOZE

Walcheren Winter 6
SBS

Walcheren Winter 7
SBS

Walcheren Winter 8 Maystar
Excellent English overwintering type with solid pure white heads for cutting from early May. (EWK)
BREE; EWK; JOHN; SBS

Walcheren Winter Aprilex see Aprilex
Walcheren Winter Arminda see Arminda
Walcheren Winter Markanta see Markanta
Walcheren Winter Maya see Maya
Wallaby
For heading late September-early October, this variety is outstanding for its top quality solid white curds. The well-protected heads are ideal for freezing. (Sutt)
JWB; MOLE; OGC; SBS; SMM; SUTT; T&M; TOZE; TUCK; WALL; YATE

Westmarsh Early see Angers No 2
White Ball
Very white, deep curd with good covering leaves. May be autumn sown without going blind. A relatively new variety but already very popular. (Foth)
FOTH

F1 White Dove
YATE

White Fox
Matures September/October. Fine curds, long standing ability. (JWB)
BREE; JOHN; JWB; SBS

White Pearl
YATE

White Rock
White Rock produces plenty of outer and inner leaves which protect the curd, it is very adaptable and is grown for the mild-July to October period. (Brwn)
BREE; BRWN; JOHN; JWB; MOLE; SBS; TOZE

White Satin
BREE

White Summer
Produces firm, round heads of excellent quality for late summer and early autumn cutting. This variety has proved very reliable even under adverse weather conditions. (Unwi)
BREE

F1 Whitney
RSLU

Celeriac

F1 Woomera
Toze; Yate

F1 Yann 37
Toze

Yopal see Zara
F1 Zara
Toze

Zero
SbS

Celeriac

Apium graveolens
Botanically identical to celery, but grown for the swollen roots rather than for the leaf stalks.

Alabaster
John; SbS

Albaster see Alabaster
Balder
The roots of this vegetable are delicious, having a pronounced celery flavour which adds greatly to the enjoyment of salads. Easily grown and requires no earthing up. Late in the season strip off the foliage, dry the roots carefully and store them in a dry shed. (OGC)
Chil; OGC; SbS

Boule de Marbre see Marble Ball
Brilliant
Productive variety produces smooth roots with beautiful white flesh which does not discolour as so many other varieties tend to. More commonly known as Turnip Rooted Celery. (Dob)
Dob

Correcta
True growers' variety, producing a large, smooth root. Gives a high yield of white-fleshed roots. Disease-resistant. (Bakk)
Bakk

Giant Prague
Globe shaped roots for use in salads. Quick growing and very tasty. (EWK)
Bakk; CGar; D&D; EWK; JWB; Mole; Rog; SbS; Suff; Tuck; VanH; Wall

Iram
Very clean, medium-sized, globe-shaped roots with few side growths. Easy to store and the flesh remains white after cooking. (Unwi)
> UNWI

Marble Ball
Turnip-shaped roots with the taste of celery and easier to grow. Keeps well all winter. (Foth)
> BRWN; FOTH; SBS; SMM

Monarch
The most widely grown variety for its smooth skin and tender flesh. (Bree)
> BREE; SBS; T&M; TOZE; YATE

Snow White
Early, with very white flesh; large size. Superb nutty flavour. (Mars)
> MARS

Tellus
Quick-growing, round roots with firm white flesh. Does not discolour when boiled. (Sutt)
> SUTT

Celery

American Green see Greensnap
Autumn Gold
Extremely long holding ability, superb resistance to pithiness and the petioles are long, quite broad with little string. (Foth)
> SBS

Avonpearl
A mid-season self-blanching variety, clear white colour. (OGC)
> CGAR; OGC; ROG; SBS; SUFF

Brydon's Prize Red see Giant Red
Brydon's Prize White
A popular strain of excellent quality. (JWB)
> JWB

Celebrity
Crisp, early and bolt resistant, with plenty of vigour. The sticks are heavier than Lathom and less stringy than any variety. Excellent for an autumn crop, but can also be grown earlier in a cool greenhouse or cold frame. (Mars)
> BRWN; DOB; MARS; MOLE; SBS; YATE

Celery

Chatteris see Lathom Self Blanching
Chinese Celery
Wild celery from China is more delicately flavoured and smaller than native types. Very hardy but can also be grown under glass. (OGC)
    OGC

Clayworth Pink see Giant Pink
Clayworth Prize Pink see Giant Pink
Fenlander see Hopkins Fenlander
Galaxy
Outstanding quality and flavoured stems. Thicker, stays stringless longer than any other variety. Can be sown early without running to seed and stands ready to harvest a long time. (T&M)
    T&M

Giant Pink
A fine crisp pink variety which blanches easily and quickly. (Suff)
    BRWN; JOHN; JWB; SBS; SUFF; SUTT

Giant Red
Large, solid and of good quality - will usually stand well into the New Year. (Mars)
    CGAR; CHIL; EWK; JOHN; MARS; MOLE; SBS; UNWI; WALL; YATE

Giant Solid White
    MOLE

Giant White
Solid, crisp and of superior flavour. Unsurpassed for table use. (Dob)
    BRWN; CHIL; D&D; DOB; EWK; ROG; SBS; VANH; WALL

Golden Self Blanching see Golden Self Blanching 3
Golden Self Blanching 3
A delicious, self-blanching celery with sturdy stalks which can be used as a salad, in savouries and as an exclusive cooked vegetable. (Bakk)
    BAKK; CART; CGAR; CHIL; D&D; DOB; EWK; FOTH; JOHN; JWB; MOLE; OGC; ROG; SBS; SUTT; TUCK; VANH; WALL

Golden Spartan
    SBS

Green
For a change, grow a green celery! This variety has excellent flavour, is very tender and crisp. (OGC)
Green Light
    SBS

Green Sleeves
A new selection of the increasingly popular green celery. Long, smooth, succulent stems are produced in profusion in late summer and autumn. (Dob)
Dob; T&M

Green Utah
For a change, grow a green celery! This variety has excellent flavour, is very tender and crisp. (OGC)
Brwn; EWK; JWB; OGC

Greenlet
RSLU

Greensnap
Rog; SbS

Groene Pascal see White Pascal
Harvest Moon
SbS

Hopkins Fenlander
Excellent, long stemmed, white, market growers' variety. Very bulky sticks, crisp and full of flavour. Slightly hardier than most sorts. (Mars)
Mars; SbS; T&M; Toze

Ivory Tower
Long, white, fleshy stems which are smooth and not stringy. (Foth)
Foth; Sutt

Jason Self Blanching see Lathom Self Blanching
Lathom Self Blanching
Outstanding, self-blanching celery with excellent flavour and high yield, coupled with reluctance to bolt. An excellent pre-pack variety for glasshouse and outdoor cropping. (Bree)
Bree; John; Mole; SbS; Toze; Unwi

Loret
RSLU

Mammoth Pink
CGar; Rob

Mammoth Pink see Giant Pink
Mammoth White
CGar; Rob

Celery

Martine
    CGar; Rob

Pearly Queen
    SbS

Red Claret see Tall Utah 52/70
Selfire
    SbS

Shamrock
    SbS

Sioux
A green celery for autumn harvesting. Has good holding ability even late in the season. Replaces Tall Utah. (Bree)
    Bree; SbS

Solid Pink
A fine variety which blanches fairly easily and quickly and will stand some late frosts. (OGC)
    OGC

Solid White
The stems of this variety are crisp, solid and of good flavour. Excellent for table use or for exhibition. (OGC)
    OGC; Sutt

Soup Celery d'Amsterdam
An indispensable, very tasty leaf celery for flavouring soups. Highly aromatic and prolific. (Bakk)
    Bakk; John

Stardust
    SbS

Tall Utah 52-70
The most cultivated growers' variety at present. Tall Utah gives an excellent production of heavy celery of A1 quality. (Bakk)
    Bakk; RSlu; SbS; Toze

Triumph
Tall growing plants produce succulent green stems which are an excellent addition to salads, soup and stews. Maturing late summer, early autumn, cropping may be extended by covering with cloches. (Sutt)
    John; Sutt

Unrivalled Pink see Giant Pink
Utah 52-70 see Tall Utah 52-70
F1 Victoria
DOB; MARS; MOLE; TOZE; WALL

White Pascal
Large, solid, white heads, best grown in trenches. (EWK)
EWK; JOHN; SBS

Chicory
Cichorium intybus
Two sorts are grown, the forcing, sugarloaf types and the heading types, often called radicchio

Apollo
Much easier to grow than traditional varieties because the white chicons remain compact with a soil covering. Distinctive flavour. (Mars)
MARS

Brussels Witloof see Witloof
Crystal Head
Excellent in autumn salads. Crisp, green lettuce-like leaves. Quick and easy to grow. (Foth)
BAKK; FOTH; UNWI

F1 Flash
BAKK; T&M

Gradina
SBS

Mechelse Medium-early
For cultivation without soil on top. Easy to grow in not too warm (up to 17-18øC), dark surroundings (under black plastic). (Bakk)
BAKK

Pain de Sucre see Sugar Loaf
Pan di Zucchero see Sugar Loaf
Robin
Bred from crossing a witloof chicory with a radicchio, Robin is cultivated and forced in exactly the same way as Witloof but produces unusual and attractive red chicons with white veins. The chicons are somewhat looser than ordinary witloof. (Bree)
BREE

Chicory Radicchio

Snowflake
Autumn and winter fresh salad vegetable. Easy to grow, no forcing or blanching needed. Grow just like lettuces, sowing in June/July for 2-3 lb. crisp, tight heads, like large Cos lettuces, in late autumn and winter. Can be stored in the fridge or a shed for up to 3 months. (T&M)
> T&M

Sugar Loaf
A quick growing large headed variety for Winter salads. (D&D)
> EWK; JWB; OGC; Rog; SbS; SMM; Suff; Sutt; Tuck; Wall

Videna
> Bakk

Winter Fare
Rather like a large Cos lettuce in appearance, provides lots of crunchy, creamy, green heads ready to eat during late autumn and early winter. (Dob)
> Dob

Winter Fare see Snowflake
Witloof
Mostly grown for Winter forcing to produce pale green chicons. (D&D)
> Bakk; CGar; Chil; D&D; EWK; John; JWB; Mole; OGC; Rog; SbS; Suff; Tuck; Wall

F1 Zoom
> Bree; Dob; Suff

Chicory Radicchio
A Grumolo Verde
Round-leaved rosette shaped plant in winter; leaves blade-shaped in summer. Sow broadcast or in rows June-October. Summer leaves for salads. Stop cutting in late summer and allow the plants to develop their beautiful green rosettes for cutting in spring. Extremely hardy. (Suff)
> Suff

Alouette
Fast growing, uniform early radicchio type. Medium size heads are a good red and well protected by larger green outer leaves. (Foth)
> Foth; T&M

Augusta
> John

Bianca di Milano

When mature forms crisp elongated head or white and green leaves, almost self blanching. Use as cut and come again crop (at 2 in.) or thin plants to 6 in. for maturing. Fairly hardy and will normally over-winter outdoors or in an unheated greenhouse, especially when treated as "cutting" crop. (Suff)

SUFF

Biondissima di Trieste

Green, smooth round-leaved chicory. Used mainly as cut and come again crop. Sow spring to summer. The plants make rapid regrowth. Can also be used in winter, when small heads form. Reasonably hardy. (Suff)

SUFF

Cesare

A mid-late variety with medium round heads and green outer leaves. Sow in July. (Suff)

JOHN; SUFF

Chioggia see Alouette

Giulio

Early compact round red heads with good bolting tolerance. Sow in May. (Suff)

JOHN; SUFF

F1 Jupiter

TOZE

Magdeburg

A large rooted variety used for blending with coffee. Lift the roots in autumn, cut into small sections and dry. May then be ground. (Suff)

SBS; SUFF

Marsica

Good tolerance of tipburn inducing conditions. (Bree)

BREE

F1 Medusa

BAKK; TOZE; YATE

Palla di Fuoco

An excellent variety for summer and autumn heading. Sow from March onwards. Firm round red heads with white veining. Very decorative. (Suff)

SUFF

Palla rossa

Red-leaved chicory for Winter salads. (D&D)

EWK; SMM; WALL

Chicory Radicchio

Palla rossa Zorzi precoce
Red-leaved chicory for Winter salads. (D&D)
    CART; CHIL; D&D; JWB; MARS; ROG; SBS; SUTT; TUCK; UNWI

Poncho
    JOHN

Prima Rossa
    YATE

Prima Rossa Special
    YATE

Red Treviso see Rossa di Treviso
Red Verona see Rossa di Verona
Red devil
Large red heads produce colourful leaves with attractive white veining and a distinctive taste. Best sown in late June and July for autumn harvesting. Has good resistance to early frosts. (Dob)
    DOB

Rossa di Treviso
Somewhat similar to White Chicory but it is less compact. Strong variety that will tolerate light frost well. (Bakk)
    BAKK; OGC; SUFF

Rossa di Verona
Forms a loose head in autumn and will crop again the following spring provided it is protected from severe frost. (Bakk)
    BAKK; OGC; SBS; SUFF

Scarpia
Improvement of the well-known sugar loaf varieties. Should not be sown before the summer or it will bolt. (Bakk)
    BAKK

Variegata di Castelfranco
A wonderfully decorative chicory with green leaves blotched red and forming an inner loose head of red and white in autumn. An ancient variety developed in the 18th century in the Castelfranco region of northern Italy. One of the best for eating quality. Best results requires forcing during winter like Witloof. (Suff)
    CHIL; SUFF

Variegata di Chioggia
Foliage green in summer, becoming red and white variegated in the cold weather. Sow broadcast or in rows, July-Aug. For use primarily in late autumn and early winter. Most suitable for forcing. Use in salads or cooked. (Suff)
    SUFF

Variegata di Sottomarina Precoce
A really unusual and decorative chicory becoming red speckled with white when mature. Another old variety named after the coastal town just south of Venice. (Suff)

    SUFF

Chinese Artichoke

Stachys affinis
Slightly fiddlier than Jerusalem artichokes (to which they are not related) but with a flavour altogether more delicate. Joy Larkcom says they are nutty and reminiscent of globe artichokes, new potatoes and water chestnuts.

Chinese Artichoke
Sweet and crisp white tubers. Excellent as a Winter vegetable, either raw, boiled, fried or pickled. (Poyn)

    FUTU; POYN

Crosnes
A culinary sensation. The peculiar tubers with the series of rings are harvested in late autumn. The flavour resembles that of artichoke bottoms. One tuber will yield at least 25 tubers. (Bakk)

    BAKK

Chinese Broccoli

Brassica oleracea var. alboglabra
Also known as Chinese kale, Gai Lan and Kailan are the Mandarin and Cantonese names for this vegetable, rather than varieties in their own right. Very accomodating in its climatic requirements.

F1 Green Lance
    CGAR; CHIL; D&D; EWK; OGC; OGC; SBS; SMM

Kailan
Not a variety name.
    SBS; SMM; SUFF

Kintsai
Vivid green and unique aroma when cooked. Summer sowing, ready after two months. (D&D)
    CGAR; D&D; EWK; SBS; SMM; SUFF

Chinese Chives
Allium tuberosus
Chinese leek and garlic chives are other common names for this vegetable, almost all parts of which are used.

Broadleaf
Distinct, mild garlic-flavour, widely varying culinary uses, harvestable three-quarters of the year. (T&M)
CHIL; D&D; EWK; T&M

Chinese Chives
Also known as Garlic Chives or Chinese Leeks producing clumps of narrow, flat leaves of delicate mild garlic flavour. Easily grown, having star-like flowers in summer. Leaves, stems, flower buds and flowers are all edible. (Dob)
DOB; FUTU; SMM

Chinese Yam
Dioscorea batatas
A hardy yam which can be grown outside in a hot sunny position, this plant produces long twining stems and large root tubers with a delicious, potato-like flavour. The tubers take several years to reach a large size but do not become woody. After harvest, the top section of the tuber can be replanted and will grow again if conditions are suitable.

Chinese Yam
FUTU

Choy Sum
Flowering brassicas, of many species.
All are brassicas, grown for their flowers. Joy Larkcom divides them into six different groups. Choy Sum, or Pak Tsoi Sum, is flowering white cabbage. Hong Tsoi Sum, or Hon Tsai tai, is purple flowered choy sum. Flowering Pak Choi is a variety of Pak Choi grown for its flowers. Edible Oil Seed Rapes are not the rapes grown in the west, but are a source of oil for lamps and cooking, and leaves and buds for eating. Hybrid Flowering Rapes are a new development from Japan, which Joy Larkcom says are the best members of the tribe for the gardener. And Brocoletto types are similar to the broccoli raab grown in southern Europe.

F1 Bouquet
CGAR; D&D; EWK; OGC; SBS; SMM; SUFF

Choy Sum (Purple Flowered)
Edible purple ribbed stems and leaves and yellow flowers. A decorative plant which tastes best when lightly boiled. (OGC)
OGC; SMM

Hon Tsai Tai
Not a true variety name.
BAKK; CHIL

Chrysanthemum Greens

Chrysanthemum coronarium
Shungiku is the Japanese name for these members of the daisy family, which are also known as Chop Suey Greens and Japanese Greens. There are two basic types, those with small, serrated leaves and those with larger, broader leaves.

Shungiku
Shungiku is the Japanese name for Chrysanthemum Greens in general, not a single variety.
CGAR; CHIL; D&D; DOB; EWK; FUTU; JOHN; OGC; SBS; SMM; SUFF

Corn Salad

Valerianella locusta
Also known as Lamb's Lettuce, it is a useful salad crop for the winter months.

Bubbles
WALL

Cavallo
Keeps on producing a mass of fresh flavoured, deep green leaf. A late summer sowing will guarantee winter salads as it is very hardy too. (T&M)
T&M

Corn Salad
A hardy quick growing salad vegetable for winter use. Sow in autumn for winter use. (D&D)
CGAR; CHAM; D&D; EWK; FOTH; FUTU; MOLE; POYN; SMM; TUCK; WALL

D'Olanda see Grote Noordhollandse
Grote Noordhollandse
Also known by the much nicer name of Lambs Lettuce, this is used when young and crisp as a salad plant, particularly useful in winter and spring. Very hardy, it has the great advantage that it can be grown using the sow-and-forget technique. Harvest whole when the plant has grown three or four pairs of leaves. (Chil)
BAKK; BREE; CHIL; DOB; JOHN; JWB; OGC; SBS; SBS; SUFF; SUTT

Cress

Jade
A robust variety which is resistant to mildew. Tasty salad ingredient for the Winter months. (Mars)
> MARS

Louviers
Fine-seeded, spoon-shaped corn salad. Beautiful, dark green colour. An extremely tasty, high-yielding corn salad variety. Very hardy. (Bakk)
> BAKK

Verte de Cambrai
A traditional French variety. Sow in rows or broadcast. Harvest complete rosettes at 6 to 8 leaves and use whole in a salad. Very decorative and unusual. (Suff)
> OGC; SUFF

Vit
The most vigorous variety for spring and autumn crops, and over wintering. Long glossy green leaves. Delicious tender mild minty flavour. (Suff)
> SUFF

Volhart
Fine-seeded. An old, well-tried variety, still highly valued by many people. Bright green colour. Much recommended variety for the expert leisure-time vegetable grower. (Bakk)
> BAKK

Cress
Many species
Various species, including salad rape and mustard, are also known and sold as cress.

American Land
This is very like water cress both in taste and appearance but can be grown in ordinary garden soil. Excellent for salads and sandwiches. (Dob)
> BAKK; CGAR; CHAM; CHAM; CHIL; D&D; DOB; EWK; FUTU; JOHN; JWB; MARS; OGC; POYN; ROG; SBS; SMM; SUFF; SUTT; T&M; TUCK; UNWI; VANH; WALL

Armada
Ready 3 days earlier than other cress - at the same time as mustard. Leaves twice the size of the common varieties and a beautiful deep green. (Mars)
> MARS

Broad Leaved
> JOHN

Curled
The ordinary type often grown in pots on the window sill, but it can be grown in the garden without trouble. (D&D)
> CGAR; CHIL; D&D; MARS; ROG; SUTT; WALL

Extra Curled
All-the-year-round, nutritious salad crop. Grow outdoors in the summer and inside during the winter. (T&M)
> T&M

Extra Double Curled
Popular for salads and garnishing. Use at once when full grown. (Dob)
> DOB

Extra Fine Moss Curled
> JOHN

Fine Curled
Dwarf growing strain with fine very well curled leaves. (EWK)
> CART; EWK; FOTH; SBS; SUFF; UNWI; YATE

Greek
A completely new addition for the mixed salad. Delicious peppery taste. A fast growing salad crop that can be broadcast in succession and cut young. (Suff)
> OGC; SUFF

Large Leaved
One of the main green salad plants. (Brwn)
> BAKK; BRWN

Plain
Large leafed type, quick growing and very productive. (EWK)
> BAKK; CGAR; EWK; JOHN; JWB; MOLE; ROG; SBS; VANH; WALL

Reform
> SBS

Super Salad
A great improvement over the ordinary type of plain-leaved cress because of its stronger stems and larger leaves. (Dob)
> DOB

Cucumber
Cucumis sativus
Generally divided into ridge, or outdoor, and frame, or indoor, types. Gherkins are smaller, and may be grown either indoors or outdoors.

Cucumber

F1 Anka
BAKK

F1 Avanti
TUCK

F1 Bella
SUTT

F1 Bronco
YATE

Chinese Long Green
Well-known variety, still very much in demand for cultivation in the open. Stays green and is disease-resistant. (Bakk)
BAKK

F1 Cordoba
SBS

F1 Crispy Salad
T&M

F1 Danimas
DOB; T&M; YATE

Delicatesse
A very famous variety, particularly suitable for pickling. Much used in salads. (Bakk)
BAKK

Delikatess see Delicatesse
F1 Farbiola
TOZE

Hoffmans Giganta
Very suitable for cultivation in the open as well as in a frame or along wires in a greenhouse. A healthy, high-yielding variety, producing heavy cucumbers. (Bakk)
BAKK

F1 Janeen
YATE

F1 Mistral
DOB

F1 Mustang
YATE

F1 Slice King
D&D; EWK; OGC

F1 Sweet Success
BAKK

F1 Uniflora
CGAR; EWK; ROG; SBS; SMM; VANH; WALL

Cucumber Frame

F1 Aidas
T&M

F1 Aramon
MOLE; SBS; WALL

F1 Athene
MARS

F1 Birgit
BAKK; BRWN; DOB; FOTH; JOHN; MOLE; SBS; TOZE

F1 Brunex
MOLE; OGC; SBS; YATE

Butcher's Disease Resistant
SBS

F1 Carmen
MOLE; SBS; T&M

Conqueror
Recommended for growing in unheated greenhouses or cold frames. Crops very well. (Dob)
DOB; OGC

F1 Cucumex
WALL

Diana
Fairly long, "All Female" indoor variety. More resistant to cold than most and a particularly good choice for a cold greenhouse. (Unwi)
UNWI

F1 Euphya
MOLE; SBS; WALL

F1 Fembaby
T&M

F1 Femdam
BRWN; CGAR; EWK; JOHN; ROG; SBS; SMM; WALL

F1 Femspot
FOTH; MOLE; SBS; SUTT; TUCK

F1 Fenumex
CGAR; D&D; EWK; OGC; ROG; SBS; SUFF; TUCK; WALL

F1 Jessica
SBS

F1 Kamaron
MOLE; SBS

King George
CGAR; ROB; WALL

F1 Landora
SUTT

F1 Lora
SBS

F1 Monique
MOLE; SBS

F1 Passander
WALL

F1 Pepinex 69
A very reliable variety for cold house and plastic tunnel culture in soil, and the very well known standard for plant sales to the amateur retail trade. The straight fruits are up to 50 cm. long, dark green, spineless, slightly ribbed with a small neck, and with excellent flavour. Resistant to gummnosis and spot disease. (Bree)
BREE; BRWN; CART; CGAR; DOB; EWK; JOHN; JWB; MARS; ROG; SBS; UNWI; WALL

F1 Petita
A mini glasshouse variety. Very high yielding, producing first quality dark green fruits. (EWK)
BRWN; CGAR; DOB; EWK; FOTH; JOHN; MOLE; OGC; ROG; SBS; SBS; SMM; SUTT; TOZE; UNWI; WALL

Rollison's Telegraph see Telegraph Improved
F1 Sandra
JOHN

Sigmadew
The fruits of this unusual variety are of excellent flavour, with thin, very pale green, almost white skin. Primarily a greenhouse cucumber, it can be grown outdoors in sheltered areas. (Sutt)
SUTT

F1 Superator
BRWN; JOHN; MOLE; SBS

F1 Sweet Alphee
SUFF

Telegraph
A well known and reliable variety with smooth-skinned, good-sized fruits. (Dob)
CART; CGAR; DOB; EWK; JOHN; JWB; MARS; OGC; SUTT; TOZE; UNWI; YATE

Telegraph Improved
A prolific cropper producing long fruits of excellent flavour. (D&D)
BRWN; D&D; FOTH; MOLE; ROG; SBS; SUFF; SUTT; TUCK; VANH; WALL

F1 Tyria
BRWN; MARS; MOLE

Cucumber Gherkin
F1 Accordia
MOLE; WALL

F1 Arena
JOHN

Beit Alpha Ellam
SBS

F1 Bestal
MARS

Boston Green
SBS

F1 Conda
UNWI

De Vorgebirg see Venlo Pickling
F1 Dex
BAKK

F1 Fanfare
FOTH

Gherkin
Very quick growing and prolific in habit. Produces a mass of small prickly fruits for pickling. (EWK)
CGAR; D&D; EWK; ROG; WALL

Cucumber Ridge

Hokus
A mixed-flowering gherkin variety, especially suitable for cultivation in the open ground. Perfect gherkin for pickling. Vigorous grower which is not prone to mosaic and gummnosis. (Bakk)
> BAKK; DOB; SBS

F1 Liberty
> T&M

National
Produces large quantities of small green fruit which should be gathered for pickling when immature. (OGC)
> OGC; SBS

Parisian Pickling
Well known variety for pickling. (Bakk)
> BAKK; JOHN; SBS

Pointsett
> SBS

Sena
Early outdoor variety, bitter free, mildew tolerant, self pollinating. (Brwn)
> BRWN

Toret
> SBS

Venlo Pickling
Well-known, still very popular growers' variety which is often used for pickling. Gives a heavy crop of beautiful gherkins. (Bakk)
> BAKK; JWB; SBS; SUTT

Vert Petit de Paris see Parisian Pickling

Cucumber Ridge

Apple Shaped
The fruits are apple shaped and are thought to be more digestable than the ordinary varieties. Easily grown out of doors, a prolific cropper. (JWB)
> JWB

Bedfordshire Prize see Long Green Ridge
Bianco Lungo di Parigi
Interestingly different is this cucumber for outdoor cultivation producing medium-sized fruits of an attractive, do-they-taste-as-good-as-they-look, creamy-white colour. Another variety to give visual appeal to the dining table. (Chil)
> CHIL

F1 Burpee Hybrid
DOB

Burpless see Burpless Tasty Green
F1 Burpless Tasty Green
CGAR; D&D; EWK; FOTH; JWB; MARS; MOLE; OGC; ROG; SBS; SUFF; SUTT; T&M; TUCK; WALL

Bush Champion
For container growing. High quality 11 in. cucumbers with a flavour much improved on greenhouse hybrids. Very compact. Crops in as little as two months from planting and yields steadily through the season in all types of weather. Mosaic resistant. (T&M)
CART; DOB; SUTT; T&M

F1 Bush Crop
BAKK; FOTH; MARS

Crystal Apple
Delightful round shaped fruits of pale colouring. Quick growing and very prolific. Reputed to be more digestible than other varieties. (EWK)
CGAR; EWK; MOLE; OGC; ROG; SBS; SMM; SUFF; SUTT; VANH; WALL

King of the Ridge
JWB

Kyoto
Good-flavoured variety producing long fruits with few seeds. Best grown on a cane tripod. (D&D)
CGAR; D&D; ROG; SBS; SUFF; T&M

Long Green Ridge
CGAR; CHIL; EWK; JOHN; ROG; SBS; SMM; SUTT; YATE

Long Prickly see Long Green Ridge
Marketeer see Marketer
Marketer
SBS

Marketmore
(Improved King of the Ridge). An outdoor slicing cucumber. Fruits up to 8 in. long. Resistant to powdery mildew and downy mildew. (Mars)
MARS; TOZE

Masterpiece
Outdoor type with large fruits of excellent taste. Highly productive. (EWK)
EWK; OGC; ROG; SBS; VANH

Dandelion

Perfection
Smaller, slightly stumpy ridge cues. Easy to grow. (Foth)
BRWN; FOTH; JOHN; MOLE; SBS; WALL

Stockwood see Long Green Ridge
F1 Tokyo Slicer
TOZE; UNWI

Yamato
Improved Japanese types for indoor or outside growing. Long thin fruits of superb flavour. (EWK)
CGAR; EWK; OGC; SBS; SMM

Dandelion

Taraxacum officinalis
The leaves, green or blanched, have long been used in salads.

A Coeur Plein
Probably the most nutritious green there is. Very rich in minerals and vitamins. Blanching under a flowerpot will take the bitterness away, or it may be forced like Witloof Chicory. (Suff)
SUFF

Broad Leaved
Excellent for salads, has valuable medicinal properties. Helps to keep everyone young. (JWB)
JWB; SBS

Salad Dandelion
Perennial. Large leaved for use in salads. Pick leaves when young. (D&D)
CGAR; CHAM; D&D

Thick-leaved
Considering we spend our lives trying to eradicate the wild form from our gardens, it is most suprising to learn just how useful this cultivated strain is. The large, thick, dark green leaves are used as a green vegetable for boiling or in a salad. For salads, though, a far more succulent can be made by blanching the hearts either by earthing up or tying the leaves together. The roots can be used for forcing or as a substitute for coffee by roasting in an oven until crisp and then grinding. Easy, vigorous and quick to grow. (Chil)
CHIL

Duck Potato
Sagittaria latifolia
An aquatic species similar to our arrowhead, the Wapato was an important food of native Americans for many centuries, The small tubers are borne on the ends of long runners and are harvested in the autumn. As they float when detached from the parent plant it is possible to scoop them off the water's surface. Native women used to collect them by wading into the water up to their chests and loosening the tubers with their toes. They can be cooked in a similar way to potatoes and have a pleasant flavour. An excellent plant for filtering eutrophic waters, as it is one of the heaviest-feeding water plants.

Duck Potato
Futu

Earth Chestnut
Bunium bulbocastaneum
A vigorous perennial that produces small tuberous roots said to taste like chestnuts when boiled. The seeds can also be used as a condiment. A rare native of chalk grasslands.

Earth Chestnut
Futu

Endive
Cichorium endivia
Related to chicory, but forming a lettuce-like head like radicchio chicory.

Avant Garde Winter
An autumn or winter endive that should not be sown too early, otherwise it might bolt. Keeps very well. Produces beautiful, robust plants. (Bakk)
Bakk

Batavian Broad Leaved see No. 5 2
Batavian Green see No. 5 2
Breedblad Volhart Winter see Avant Garde Winter
Casco d'Oro
Beautiful, heavy plants with golden-yellow heart. Tender variety for summer and autumn cultivation. (Bakk)
Bakk

Endive

Cornet De Bordeaux
A very fine old French variety which is very hardy. Provides constant cut and come again through Winter. Performs outstandingly with cold tunnel/frame culture over Winter. (Suff)
SUFF

De Ruffec
Sharp, crisp vegetable which will liven up any salad. Use with or instead of lettuce. (Foth)
FOTH; SBS

De Ruffec see Ruffec
Dolly
Bred in France where it is extremely popular. Good curl with blanched centre. Cropping period October-November. (Mole)
MOLE; SBS

Elodie
Very compact variety suitable for close spacing with a very finely divided leaf, slow bolting and easy to blanch. (Bree)
BREE

Elysee
YATE

Eminence
This variety is suitable for both indoor and outdoor production. The densely formed centres are yellow with medium to long outer broad leaves. Resistant to basal rot and strong against tipburn. Sow March to August for cropping June to October. (Brwn)
BRWN

Fijne Krul Groen see Green Curled
Fine Maraichere
A small and compact variety which is very frizzy and looks very decorative. Not hardy so should be grown in spring and summer. (Suff)
SUFF

Glory
YATE

Green Curled
Another alternative salad crop for outdoor or glasshouse use. Compact with curled heads of dark green leaves. (EWK)
CHIL; D&D; EWK; JOHN; JWB; OGC; ROG; SBS; SMM; SUTT; TOZE; TUCK; WALL

Ione
For spring to early autumn crops. Very fine curled leaves. (Toze)
    Dob; Toze

Jeti
Very uniform, large heavy heads. Upright foliage with self-blanching habit. Excellent for both summer and autumn use. (EWK)
    EWK; SbS; SMM

Markant
A large and extensively curled endive, the heart blanches up well because of the long upright leaves. An ideal variety for late sowings, performing well in late autumn conditions. Sow August for cropping late Sept/Nov. (Brwn)
    Brwn

Minerva
    Yate

Moss Curled see Green Curled
No. 5 2
A crisp and tender variety with large leaves for winter salads and excellent, too, as a cooked vegetable. (Dob)
    Bakk; Dob; John; JWB; OGC; SbS; Sutt

No. 5 Malan
    RSlu

No. 5 Sinco
Escarole or smooth leaved endive, with a large size but should not be grown wider than 30 cm. X 30 cm. in order to promote a good blanch in the hearts. (Bree)
    Bree

Oxalie
    Mole; Wall

President
A strong, curled endive for summer and early autumn cultivation, slow in running to seed. Stands bad weather very well. Top quality. (Bakk)
    Bakk

Riccia Pancalieri
Very curled leaves with rose tinted white midribs, voluminous white heart. Sow in rows from March to September, thinning to about 12 in. apart. For use in summer, autumn and winter. Self-blanching variety. (Suff)
    OGC; Suff

Fennel

Sally
Easy to grow, the plants produce tight hearts of cut, curled and crisped leaves, naturally blanched in the centre. (Mars)
> Cart; Mars; Mole; SbS; Yate

Sanda
Vigorous, strap-leaved with a frilled edge and large size, somewhat less susceptible to tipburn, to cold and to bolting than other types, suitable for glasshouse and open field culture. (Bree)
> Bree

Scarola Verde
Forms very large head with green and white leaves, curled at edges with tasty, tender white midribs. Can blanche a few days before use by tying leaves together or covering with a box or pot. Most suitable for use in spring or summer, though it may bolt in sudden heat. (Suff)
> Suff

St Laurent-Midori
Medium-sized, very full, finely curled endive. Recommended for early sowing; for summer and autumn harvest. Early maturing and quick-blanching. (Bakk)
> Bakk

Tres Fine Maraichere Coquette
Appetizing, slender very fine cut curled leaf. A notable uniform selection of the superb French variety Tres Fine Maraichere. It is a good all rounder, excellent if it is your first try at growing it. (T&M)
> RSlu; T&M

Wallonne
A special selection of this traditional French variety. Forms a large tightly packed head with self-blanching heart and finely cut leaves. Vigorous and hardy. Sow Aug-Sept for Nov-Jan harvest. Also for tunnel culture. (Suff)
> RSlu; Suff

White Curled
> Bakk

Fennel

Foeniculum vulgare var. azoricum
Florence Fennel, grown for the swollen stem bases, rather than the herb fennel.

Bronze
A handsome variety. Use the leaves in soups, sauces and fish dishes. (Poyn)
> Poyn; SbS

Cantino
Developed for its resistance to bolting from early sowing. Bulbs ready from August. Can be cooked or used raw in salads. Refreshing celery/aniseed flavour. (Mars)
MARS; OGC; SBS; SMM; SUFF; TUCK; YATE

Common
SBS

Di Firenze
This is best sown between May and July. Medium sized bulbs with delicate aniseed flavour. (OGC)
CGAR; CHIL; D&D; EWK; OGC; SBS; VANH

Fino
A bulb fennel for early crops. The variety has strong resistance to bolting. (Bree)
BAKK; BREE; DOB; FOTH; MOLE; POYN; SBS; TOZE; UNWI; YATE

Florence see Di Firenze
Green
POYN

Herald
Plump, sweet anise-flavour bulbs. In trials it has shown a marked improvement in bolt resistance over all other varieties. Recommended for earlier and successional sowings. (T&M)
T&M

Perfection
Sow from May to July. Fairly resistant to bolting and produces medium sized bulbs with delicate aniseed flavour. (Suff)
SUFF

Sirio
An Italian bred variety which produces large white solid bulbs on compact plants. Very sweet flavour and quite aromatic. (Sutt)
SUTT

Sweet Florence see Di Firenze
Tardo
A bulb fennel for early crops. Strong resistance to bolting. (Bree)
BREE; TOZE

Zefa Fino see Fino
Zefa Tardo see Tardo

French Bean Climbing

Phaseolus vulgaris

Blue Lake White Seeded

Requires sticks or a climbing frame. Very productive and suitable for home freezing with an excellent flavour. Pods can also be dried for use as haricot. (OGC)

BREE; BRWN; CHIL; D&D; DOB; EWK; FOTH; JOHN; JWB; MOLE; OGC; ROG; SBS; SMM; SUFF; SUTT; TUCK; VANH; WALL

Borlotto

Unusual and attractive, the 6in. flat and broad pods are pale green with red stripes. When young the pods are cut and eaten as a normal french bean, left they may be shelled and the seeds eaten. (Foth)

FOTH

Borlotto Lingua di Fuoco

This is the original Fire Tongue strain from Italy. May be eaten as green pods but grown mainly for delicious semi-dry beans and dry beans. Spectacular green pods with red stripes make this very decorative. (Suff)

SUFF

Burro d'Ingegnoli

Traditional Italian variety unknown in the UK. Large flat yellow pods of excellent fleshy and stringless quality. Sweet and deliecious. 78 days. (Suff)

SUFF

Corona d'Oro

A climbing bean giving heavy yields of golden-yellow pods, round in section and succulent and tender in texture. Regular picking will encourage further pod formation of this useful and decorative variety. (John)

EWK; JOHN; ROG

Cristal

YATE

Florint

MOLE

Glastada

RSLU

Goldmarie

SUTT

Helda
    BAKK; RSLU; TOZE

Hunter
Flat podded variety. Yields heavy crops of long straight, stringless pods. (Foth)
    BRWN; D&D; EWK; FOTH; JOHN; MARS; OGC; ROG; SUFF; SUTT; TUCK; VANH; WALL

Kentucky Blue
Excellent flavour and yields. Pods smooth and fleshy 16-17cm. (Bree)
    BREE; T&M

Kingston Gold
    ROB

Kronos
    BREE; MOLE

Kwintus
Despite the seed bulges which tend to be produced, the 9-11in. pods are tender, have a delicious distinctive flavour and are usually stringless. (Dob)
    MOLE

Largo
A smashing variety growing tall like a runner bean but producing round, stringless delicious pods. (Foth)
    MARS; UNWI

Limka
    YATE

Marvel of Venice see Or du Rhin
Mechelse Markt
Very much recommended to those who like a bean that is not too fleshy. Mechelse Markt produces clusters of so-called single beans which are unequalled as regards their fine flavour. Exceptionally heavy-cropping variety. (Bakk)
    BAKK

Meraviglia di Venezia see Or du Rhin
Musica
Wide, flat, stringless pods with a delicious true beany flavour. Sown early it crops weeks before outdoor crops. Can also be sown outdoors. (T&M)
    MOLE; T&M

Neckargold
    DOB

Neckarkoenigin
A long thick bean which can be used for slicing as well as for breaking. It will give a high yield per plant. Very resistant to diseases. (Bakk)

BAKK

Or du Rhin
A very fine old variety with broad flat yellow pods. Delicious picked young and cooked whole, also used in minestrone and for fresh shelling beans. The crispest and tastiest bean we have tried. Black seeded. A late maincrop. (Suff)

BAKK; OGC; SUFF

Pea Bean
The flat pods should be harvested young to eat whole, or shelled out like peas. Alternatively, leave to dry. Attractive bi-coloured seed. (OGC)

EWK; OGC; SBS; SUFF

Purple King
Excellent early crops of purple pods for both glasshouses or outdoor production. Will harvest over a long period. (EWK)

EWK; JOHN; ROG

Purple Podded see Purple Podded Climbing
Purple Podded Climbing
Decorative and delicious, ht. approx. 150cm. (5ft). (Sutt)

CGAR; ROG; SUTT

Rakker
Unquestionably the highest yielding variety producing record crops! Early and extremely prolific. Thick, fleshy beans with a delicious flavour. Rakker is also suitable for cultivation in a greenhouse. (Bakk)

BAKK

Rentmeester
A marked improvement of the old type Veense: very prolific, stringless, and with long, broad pods. Those who like a tender French bean for slicing with an outstanding flavour should not fail to try this variety. (Bakk)

BAKK

Rheingold see Or du Rhin
Robroy
A new climbing French bean, cream splashed with red. Very tender when cooked young. Good flavour and very attractive to grow. (CGar)

CGAR; ROB; WALL

Robsplash
New climbing French bean, cream splashed purple, very tender when cooked young. (CGar)
CGAR; ROB

Romano
Long, fleshy, tender, meaty and stringless pods, liberally loaded with flavour. (T&M)
T&M

Viola Cornetti
Typical Italian climbing bean with fine stringless purple podded beans. (OGC)
OGC; SUFF

Violet Podded Stringless
The pods are round, fleshy and tender with an excellent taste. Decorative dark purple pods change to green when boiled. (Foth)
BAKK; FOTH

Wachs Goldstrahl
A long, thick-fleshed bean which produces a high yield of beautiful, golden-yellow pods. First class selection. (Bakk)
BAKK

Westlandia
A very richly bearing variety, producing beans in clusters of 4 to 6. The tasty beans are long and beautifully shaped. They have a dark green colour. An excellent, healthy vegetable. (Bakk)
BAKK

French Bean Dwarf

Acapulco
RSLU

Admires
Excellent dwarf French bean (large podded) for slicing. Early and very prolific. Admires is very much in demand, especially because of its resistance to many diseases. A variety with a very fine flavour. (Bakk)
BAKK

Allure
Dark green pod, long and slender; very productive. Resistant to most occurring bean diseases. (Bakk)
BAKK

French Bean Dwarf

Annabel
Stringless, flavoursome, slim pods 4-5in. in length borne in profusion. This compact item is ideal for the smaller garden and may also be grown in growing bags on the patio. (Dob)
CGAR; DOB; EWK; ROG; TUCK; WALL

Aramis
Combines the high quality and flavour of the French "filet" types, with the high yield and concentrated podset of modern breeding. Very fine, round, stringless pods 14-15cm. in length. Pods are medium green colour with purple markings which disappear on cooking. (Bree)
BREE; T&M; UNWI

Atlantica
Try this if you want high yields, a rich distinctive flavour and something a little different. Broad, flat juicy pods fleshy and stringless, a type much grown in the USA and Europe, delicious served sliced or whole. (T&M)
T&M

Bafin
This is like a true French haricot vert but stringless. It produces pencil slim, short beans ideal for freezing. (OGC)
OGC; ROG

Black Prince
SBS; WALL

Brown Dutch
One of the best drying beans. Floury texture and an excellent flavour. Easy to grow, and easy to shell. (Suff)
BAKK; OGC; ROG; SUFF

Bush Blue Lake
ROG

Canadian Wonder
Old established variety, producing very heavy crops of flat shaped pods. (EWK)
CGAR; D&D; EWK; JOHN; JWB; MAS; OGC; ROG; SBS; WALL

Cascade
JOHN; MOLE; ROG; WALL

Chevrier Vert
The classic French Flageolet dating from 1880. Tasty and tender greeny white fresh beans for classic French dishes. (Suff)
BAKK; SUFF

Chinese Yellow
Drying bean. It is extremely resistant to less favourable weather conditions. Gives
a heavy crop of yellow beans which turn white when cooking. (Bakk)
  BAKK

Clyde
"Fine" whole bean, with good vigour and slightly early. Suitable for fresh market.
(Bree)
  BREE

Contender
Very early and productive. Useful for both the private gardener and the commer-
cial grower. Can also be used as a haricot. (OGC)
  BAKK; MAS; OGC; ROG; SBS; SHAR

Cropper Teepee
As Purple, except the round pods are slightly larger, and medium green and white
seeded. An excellent variety with disease resistance. (Foth)
  FOTH; JOHN; ROG

Daisy
The long, stringless beans are held above the leaves so they are very easy to pick
and are not splashed by soil. Excellent for freezing. (Mars)
  MARS; T&M

Delinel
Ultra-fine deep green beans, with a unique texture and true French flavour. Heavy-
cropping, it is one of the first of its type that is perfectly stringless. (Mars)
  MARS

Deuil Fin Precoce
Compact plants ideal for cloche work, produce a good crop of steely grey-green
pods with unique delicacy of flavour. (OGC)
  OGC; ROG; SUFF

Dutch Princess
  VANH

Early Wax see Earlybird
Earlybird
A golden yellow podded variety which produces straight, fleshy pods, 6in. in length.
Wax or yellow podded varieties are gaining in popularity, not only for their novelty
value but also because of their excellent flavour and succulent texture. (John)
  JOHN; ROG

French Bean Dwarf

Erato
Medium early, yellow-fleshed dwarf French bean, resistant to fairly bad weather conditions and, therefore, a sure cropper. Good-yielding variety. (Bakk)
BAKK

Fin de Bagnol
The old gourmet needle bean with delicious fine round pods which can be used as filet or snap beans. 52 days. (Suff)
SUFF

Flageolet Chevrier see Chevrier Vert
Forum
High cold tolerance. High quality beans even in difficult conditions. Very useful in cold wet springs, resistance to halo blight CBMV and anthracnose. (T&M)
BREE; T&M; WALL

Golden Rocky
ROG

Golden Sands
Long pods which crop over a long period. Very good flavour. (EWK)
CGAR; EWK; OGC; TUCK; VANH

Gresham
MOLE; ROG

Groene Flageolet see Chevrier Vert
Harvester
Good for freezing or for dry haricot beans. (Barb)
JWB; ROG

Horsehead
Particulary suitable for growing in the UK. The dark red bean seeds are excellent for inclusion in soups, casseroles and chile con carne. Taken young pods can be eaten like conventional French beans. (OGC)
OGC

Kent
BREE

Keygold
BAKK

Kinghorn Wax
Medium-size, stringless, round, yellow wax beans with a fine flavour. (Foth)
SUTT

Larma
Very long-podded bean, 20-25cm. A richly bearing variety, highly resistant to diseases. (Bakk)
BAKK

Lasso
An early maturing Kenyan fine bean, widely used by commercial growers in the UK and on the continent for the high yields of medium green, round crispy pods. Best eaten at approx. 4ins they can be cooked whole or sliced. Good plant vigour will give yields to October from late sowings. (Foth)
FOTH

Laura
TOZE; YATE

Limelight
Earliest bush bean. Exceptionally thick, fleshy fibreless and broad pods with a distinctive sweet flavour. Can be sown mid-summer for a heavy autumn crop. Also the shelled beans are delicious fresh or dried. (T&M)
T&M

Loch Ness
SBS

Masai
Flavour best of all. Ultra slim pods. Pick handfuls at a time of slim, extra fine, fillet beans a mere 0.25ins. wide, of superlative quality with distinctive, gourmet flavour. This is the variety grown in places like Kenya to supply the international restaurant trade. An excellent, sturdy, garden variety, early and high yielding, with good disease and cold tolerance. (T&M)
BREE; T&M

Masterpiece Stringless
An improved, stringless development of Masterpiece for slicing. Very early. (Mars)
CART; MARS; T&M; UNWI

Maxidor
A marked improvement on the old yellow-fleshed varieties. Very rich-bearing dwarf French bean. Healthy variety. An excellent addition to the existing range. (Bakk)
BAKK

Maxima
BREE

Mirage
Produces long, fine-seeded dark green beans. This delicious dwarf French bean is extremely disease-resistant. A guaranteed sure cropper. (Bakk)
BAKK

French Bean Dwarf

Mont d'Or
Probably the finest flavoured golden wax with stringless flat pods. A very old French variety. Seed black. (Suff)
JWB; MARS; MOLE; OGC; ROG; SUFF

Mont d'Or Golden Butter see Mont d'Or

Montano
Round, dark green pods 15 cm. in length, stringless excellent for freezing. (Brwn)
BAKK; BRWN; JOHN; MOLE; ROG; SHAR; YATE

Narbonne
RSLU

Nassau
A flat podded French bean of the romano type. The pods are stringless and of very high quality with better flavour than most snap beans. (OGC)
BRWN; JOHN; OGC; ROG; SHAR; SUTT

Nerina
A unique and very special variety with very slim and stringless, well flavoured non-fading dark green pods which stay smooth longer and freeze well. Erect habit for easy picking and resistant to CBMV. (T&M)
JOHN; ROG; RSLU; T&M

Odessa
A very high yielding modern small podded variety ideal for the home gardener and for freezing and cooking whole. The pods are bright green in colour, rounded in section and have a maximum length of 5in. Pod quality is excellent with slow seed development, the flavour is superb. (John)
BAKK; JOHN; ROG

Othello
An extremely fine-podded bean, also called "faux-filet". Othello is a needle bean, approx. 12cm. in length and with a cross-section of only approx 4-6mm. when picked young. First-class bean for gourmets. An impressive cropper. (Bakk)
BAKK

Primel
MARS

Processor
White seeded variety which can be used as a haricot bean when dried. (EWK)
MOLE; ROG; WALL

French Bean Dwarf

Pros
Excellent when picked regularly and eaten fresh, but also bred with the freezer in mind. Each plant bears quantities of round, sweet, juicy pods about 4-5in. long. When the first pods reach this size and can still be cleanly snapped between the fingers, the whole plant can be lifted, the beans removed and frozen whole, not sliced or chopped. (Dob)
> DOB; MARS; UNWI

Provider
An early green round podded bean with delicious fleshy 5 in. long pods. Yield of the compact plants is good even in bad weather conditions. Pods remain fresh long after picking. One of the good reliable older varieties. (Suff)
> ROG; SHAR; SUFF

Purple Queen
One of the best flavours. A heavy yielder of glossy purple stringless beans. The round pods cook to an appetising dark green. (Foth)
> BAKK; FOTH; ROG; SMM; SUTT; UNWI; WALL

Purple Teepee
Fine flavoured, stringless pods are held high, for easy picking, turning rich green in boiling water. Very productive, quick to mature making it suitable for late, catching up sowings. (T&M)
> FOTH; OGC; SUFF; T&M

Radar
A new, slim podded variety of the type favoured by gourmet restaurants because the young pods are tender, full of flavour and quite stringless. A multipodded type which can be picked in bunches at the 4in. stage and cooked without slicing. (T&M)
> T&M

Record
A fairly early double dwarf French bean which will tolerate some cold. Well-known variety, still very much in demand. (Bakk)
> BAKK

Regina
Drying bean. A vigorous grower, clearly recognizable by the red-coloured pods. The dried beans are decoratively spotted in red and have a marbled appreance. (Bakk)
> BAKK

Rocquencourt
Lovely dark yellow long round/oval pods contrasting with dark green foliage. This variety is especially resistant to cold growing conditions. 64 days. (Suff)
> SUFF

Roma II
One of the most widely grown beans in the business. Medium large fleshy pods that are traditionally cut in USA and Europe but can be served sliced or whole. (Bree)
> BREE

Royalty
Distinctive purple pods which turn green when cooked. Heavy crops of stringless beans with excellent flavour. (OGC)
> CGAR; CHIL; D&D; EWK; JWB; OGC; ROG; SUFF; TUCK

Safari
> SUTT

Saxa
> BAKK

Slenderette
Really outstanding for its heavy crop of thick fleshy stringless pods. Strong-growing variety which crops over a long period. (Sutt)
> ROG; SHAR

Sprite
Dark green, pencil shaped pods. Very suitable for freezing. (EWK)
> CGAR; EWK; ROG; SBS; SUTT

St Andreas see Masterpiece
> CGAR; DOB; EWK; JOHN; JWB; MOLE; ROG; SBS; SUTT

St Andreas see Masterpiece
Sungold
> ROG

Sunray
A highly appreciated variety for Market Growers as well as for Home Gardeners. Dark green pods which are excellent for deep freezing, stringless. (Brwn)
> BRWN; JOHN; ROG; YATE

Tavera
> RSLU

Tendercrop
Long round pods, stringless, crisp and fleshy. They remain in good condition on the plants for a long time. (Unwi)
> UNWI

Tendergreen
Fleshy, meaty pods which are stringless and fibreless with an excellent flavour.
(T&M)
> BRWN; CART; CGAR; D&D; EWK; FOTH; JOHN; JWB; MOLE; OGC; ROG; SBS;
> SMM; SUTT; TOZE; TUCK; VANH

Teseo
> BREE

The Prince
Long slim pods with a magnificent flavour. Excellent for freezing and one of the
most widely grown varieties. (T&M)
> CART; CGAR; CHIL; D&D; DOB; EWK; FOTH; JOHN; JWB; MARS; MOLE; OGC;
> ROG; SBS; SUTT; T&M; UNWI

Torrina
Large round podded type 16cms in length. Quick to mature and pods are set high
on plants for easy picking. (EWK)
> EWK

Triomphe de Farcy
An early variety gourmet bean with distinctive purple streaks on the pods. Another real old variety improved to use as filet or snap bean. 49 days. (Suff)
> BAKK; SUFF

Valja
> JOHN; ROG

Vilbel
Very versatile with a long period of harvest. High yields of long slender, stringless
fillet, or fine, gourmet beans of excellent quality and flavour. (T&M)
> T&M

Wachs Goldperle
A juicy, succulent bean, attractive in appearance and highly esteemed by Continental cooks. The productive plants carry clusters of golden-yellow, round fleshy
pods about 5in. long. These remain tender for a good length of time. Both seeds
and flowers are white. (Dob)
> DOB

Garlic

Garlic
Allium sativum
Very easy to grow, even in U.K. climates, and often becoming more prolific as it adapts to local conditions in successive seasons.

Cristo
BIR

Garlic
The sections, or cloves of each bulb should be separated and planted just below the soil surface during February/April. Space row 6-8 in. apart and allow 4 in. between cloves. Lift the crop in July-August. Store like Shallots. (Dob)
BAKK; DOB; FOTH; OGC; POYN; SUFF; SUTT; T&M

Germidour
BIR

Long Keeper
Well adapted to the British climate. Each clove planted should produce one garlic bulb. (Mars)
MARS

Pink
Plant from November to March in light free draining soil in a sunny position. Approximately 10-12 cloves per bulb. (Tuck)
TUCK

Red Bulbed
SMM

Rocambole
Smaller red bulbed variety with a curled stem bearing bulbils. (Poyn)
POYN

Thermidrome
BIR

White Bulbed
SMM

White Pearl
ROG

Good King Henry
Chenopodium bonus-henricus
A common enough weed, but one with tasty and nutritious leaves.

Good King Henry
Perennial, 5 ft., ancient vegetable. Use young leaves like spinach, or force shoots in spring and use like asparagus. (D&D)
    CGar; Cham; Chil; D&D; EWK; Futu; John; Poyn; SbS; SMM; Suff; Unwi

Lincolnshire Spinach see Good King Henry
Mercury see Good King Henry

Groundnut

Apios americana
A hardy perennial vine that will climb to over 10 m. under ideal conditions. It produces strings of small, ovoid edible tubers that sometimes reach the size of a bantam's egg. A native of eastern North America, this plant was once cultivated by native peoples for its tasty tubers, which are similar in taste and texture to ordinary potatoes and can be eaten in much the same way. Tubers are harvested after the foliage dies down and are joined together on long strings, which makes harvesting easier. They should be stored damp or left in the ground until needed. The plants are members of the legume family and develop nitrogen-fixing nodules that can help to increase soil fertility.

American Groundnut
    Futu

Horseradish Japanese

Wasabia japonica
Matsumi
    Poyn

Huauzontli

Chenopodium berlandieri
A Mexican annual cultivated for its mild flavoured leaves which are traditionally eaten fried with onions or in salads. They produce large quatities of seeds which can be ground to make flour for tortillas or as a millet substitute. Has been suggested as a potential new grain crop. In cold weather the leaves turn red.

Huauzontli
    Futu

Huckleberry
Solanum burbankii
Annual plants that grow up to 1 m. tall and bear large quantities of 3-4 cm. diameter black berries. Prolific and easy to grow.

Garden Huckleberry
A high-yielding, easy to grow annual crop. Give the unusual half-hardy annual treatment, planting out late May or early June. The large berries are very freely produced and are delicious in pies and tarts but wait until they are really soft, black and juicy otherwise the taste is bitter. Excellent for making delicious jam. (Unwi)
UNWI

Mrs B's Garden Huckleberry
FUTU

Ice Plant
Mesembryanthemum spp
Although most people grow Mesembryanthemum for its flowers, the fleshy leaves make an interesting addition to summer salads. They also, apparently, sometimes stop forest fires in California.

Ice Plant
A low growing fleshly leaved ornamental, which makes an excellent ground cover. Leaves can be used in salads and also cooked like spinach. (OGC)
FUTU; OGC; SUFF

Jerusalem Artichoke
Helianthus tuberosus
An edible member of the Sunflower family, grown for its underground tubers. Makes an excellent cover crop.

Boston Red
Large red skinned, knobbly. (Futu)
SMM

Common
A very easy winter vegetable. Plant tubers 4 in. deep and 12 in. apart as soon as possible in spring on a sunny site. Lift as required during the winter. (Mars)
MARS

Cream
Cream skin. (SMM)
SMM

Dwarf Sunray
Tender enough that peeling of outer skin is not necessary. Dwarf and unique in that it flowers freely so can be dual purpose in the flower border. (T&M)
> Futu; T&M

Fuseau
The uniform long tubers of this variety, with a very smooth surface, are much easier to prepare in the kitchen. Delicious boiled or fried. (Mars)
> Futu; Mars; SMM

Jerusalem Artichoke
Its yellow flowers grow to a height of up to 3 metres. Potato-sized tubers grow under soil level. Delicious flavour, cooked as well as fried. An old-time vegetable. Harvest in November. (Bakk)
> Bakk; John; Tuck

Jicama
Pachyrhizus tuberosus

A Mexican vegetable that is gaining popularity in the US. Grown for its tuberous roots — the seeds are reputed to be poisonous, the reverse of Runner Beans. Highly ornamental, a climber with dense racemes of purple flowers. Growing for the roots, however, you must be steel-willed and pluck them off. The roots look like turnips but have a thirst-quenching fresh apple taste. They are sliced and sprinkled either with sugar or with salt and/or lemon juice. Alternatively, they can be used as water chestnuts in oriental cooking. Grow as a half-hardy annual and give them the warmest, sunniest spot you can spare, or let them loose in your greenhouse.

Jicama
> Chil

Kale
Brassica oleracea convar. acephala

F1 Arsis
> RSlu

F1 Bornick
> SbS

F1 Buffalo
> Bree

Cottagers
> John; SbS

Kale

F1 Darkibor
BRWN; DOB

Dwarf Green Curled
Dwarf habit with closely curled leaves. (Dob)
BAKK; BRWN; CART; CGAR; D&D; DOB; EWK; FOTH; JOHN; JWB; MARS; MOLE;
OGC; ROG; RSLU; SBS; SUFF; T&M; TUCK; UNWI; WALL; YATE

Dwarf Green Curled Scotch see Dwarf Green Curled
F1 Fribor
BRWN; CGAR; EWK; JOHN; JWB; MOLE; OGC; SBS; TOZE; TUCK; WALL

Half Tall see Dwarf Green Curled
Hungry Gap
Latest hardy variety, matures March/April when other greens are scarce. Sow up to
August where it is to mature. (Mars)
MARS; TUCK

F1 Kobolt
BREE

F1 Moosbor
JOHN

Pentland Brig
Leaves with curled edges can be harvested throughout winter. Also produces suc-
culent side shoots in early spring. (Tuck)
CGAR; EWK; JOHN; JWB; MARS; OGC; SBS; SMM; SUFF; TUCK; UNWI

F1 Showbor
DOB; JOHN

Spurt
Grow like spinach. Masses of tender deep green curly leaf for salads, steaming or
boiling. Ready in 6 weeks. (T&M)
T&M

Tall Green Curled
Similar to Dwarf Green Curled. Some tolerance to club root and cabbage root fly.
(Mars)
CGAR; JOHN; MARS; MOLE; SBS; WALL

Tall Scotch Curled see Tall Green Curled
Thousand Head
Strong-growing, hardy and prolific variety, useful both as a vegetable and for stock
feeding. (Dob)
DOB; JWB; MAS; SUFF; SUTT; TUCK; UNWI

Westland Autumn
Late-curling selection that can be harvested from December until the middle of February. Taste at its best when touched by the frost. Will even stand quite some frost. (Bakk)
> BAKK; DOB

Westland Winter Toga
A very hardy easy to grow winter vegetable with curly green leaves. This stands throughout winter. Sow April to May. Rich in vitamins. (VanH)
> VANH

Westlandse Herfst see Westland Autumn
F1 Winterbor
> EWK; FOTH; JOHN; SBS; TOZE; YATE

Kiwano

Cucumis metuliferus
Also called the Horny Cucumber, it is a close relative of the cucumber, climbs or trails in similar fashion and bears curious orange-red fruit studded with spiny protruberances. The fleshy pulp surrounding the seeds is bright green and thirst quenching. Needs similar conditions to cucumbers.

Kiwano
> CHIL; FUTU

Kohlrabi

Brassica oleracea convar. acephala
Closely related to Kale, but grown for the edible swollen stems. The leaves can also be eaten.

Blaro
Very suitable for outdoor cultivation as well as for early cultivation under glass. Fast grower that will stand some frost and hardly bolts. Very tender. (Bakk)
> BAKK; BREE

Delicacy Purple
One of the best-known kohlrabi varieties. Exceptionally fine flavour, extremely tender. Marked improvement of the so-called Vienna types. (Bakk)
> BAKK

Delikatess Blauer see Delicacy Purple
F1 Dynamo
> YATE

Komatsuna

F1 Express Forcer
  BAKK; JOHN

Green Vienna see White Vienna

F1 Kolpak
  JOHN; VANH

F1 Lanro
  BAKK; BREE; DOB; FOTH; TOZE

Purple Vienna
Produces a purple bulb. Can be sown up to August as they have some frost resist-ance. (D&D)
  BRWN; CHIL; D&D; DOB; EWK; FOTH; JOHN; JWB; MOLE; OGC; ROG; SBS; SUFF; SUTT; TUCK; WALL

Roblau
Purple-skinned version of Lanro F1 with good shape and excellent crisp flesh. (Toze)
  TOZE

Rolano
Very fast maturing variety producing succulent swollen stems approximately 8 weeks from sowing. This flavoursome item makes an interesting addition to salads when finely grated. (Dob)
  DOB

F1 Rowel
  MARS; T&M; UNWI

Superschmelz
A giant kohlrabi, soft like butter, for outdoor cultivation. Well fertilized, it can reach a weight of up to 10 kg. Stores well in a cool spot. (Bakk)
  BAKK

F1 White Danube
  OGC

White Vienna
Slightly earlier than the purple strain. Flesh has fine even texture of excellent flavour. (EWK)
  BRWN; CHIL; D&D; EWK; JOHN; JWB; MOLE; OGC; ROG; SBS; SUTT; TUCK; WALL

Komatsuna
Brassica rapa var pervidis or var. komatsuna
Also known as Mustard Spinach and Spinach Mustard, which is confusing as it is neither a mustard nor a spinach, but a flowering rape, a kind of leafy turnip.

Green Boy
SMM

Komatsuna
Fast growing leaf cabbage with mild fresh taste. (Suff)
BAKK; CGAR; D&D; EWK; FUTU; OGC; SBS; SMM; SUFF

Tendergreen
(Spinach mustard) Ready in just 20 days and regrows quickly. Excellent for freezing. Sow spring to late summer. Heat and cold tolerant. (T&M)
CHIL; T&M

Leaf Celery
Might this be a Stem Lettuce?

Cutting Celery
Very easy to grow, with the same flavour as normal celery; but produces lots of leaf, instead of stems for blanching. Ideal for soups, salads, and seasoning. Winter hardy. Produces well flavoured seed, ideal for soups &c. (Suff)
SUFF

Krul
Excellent flavour and aroma of celery is present in the leaves. Use for garnishes, salads and an additional flavour for soups and casseroles. (Foth)
FOTH

Leaf Celery
Celery flavoured leaves for salads and soup. Allow some to go to seed the following year to give stronger flavour in soups. (OGC)
D&D; OGC

Leaf Tissue
Namenia spp
Namenia
A tasty "leaf stalk vegetable". The stalks as well as the leaves can be cooked. Can be eaten virtually all season long. Extremely rich in vitamins. (Bakk)
BAKK

Leek

Allium porrum
There is no real distinction between pot leeks and blanching leeks, just that some varieties have a greater tendency to form a bulb at the base of the stem.

Alaska
An extremely winter hardy leek with dark blue-green foliage and stems 20-25 cm. long. Shows strong regrowth in spring for harvest until May, and will not bolt readily during this period. (OGC)
> JOHN; OGC; RSLU; SBS

Albinstar
Excellent variety for lifting late summer or early autumn. Long, slender shaft with light green foliage. Ideal for exhibition work. (EWK)
> BAKK; CGAR; D&D; EWK; JWB; OGC; ROG; SBS; SUTT; TUCK; WALL

Alita
> RSLU

Alma
> SBS

Ardea
> MOLE

Armor
> YATE

Autumn Giant
Autumn Giant 2 Argenta
Performs outstandingly whether sown early or late and does well over a long season. Matures in October, yet stands ready for harvest right through to May, giving high quality, thick, very heavy stems, of excellent mild flavour and yield with few bolters. (T&M)
> CART; DOB; JOHN; OGC; RSLU; SBS; T&M

Autumn Giant Rami
> TOZE

Autumn Mammoth see Goliath
Autumn Mammoth 2
> SBS; TOZE

Autumn Mammoth 2 Walton Mammoth
Large and bold, a good general purpose variety for autumn and winter. Stands winter weather conditions well. Good blanch. (Brwn)
> BRWN; MARS; SBS

Autumn Triumphator
  CGar

Bastion
  Mole; SbS; Wall

Berdina
  Bree

Bleu de Solaise see Blue Solaise
Blizzard
One of the finest new leeks available. Very winter hardy producing medium sized shafts of a fine colour and flavour through the winter months. Harvest from December to April. Blizzard is tolerant to yellow stripe virus. (VanH)
  John; Mole; SbS; VanH; Wall

Blue Green Autumn
  SbS

Blue Solaise
  Bakk; SbS

Bluestar see Giant Winter 3
Branta
  Yate

Carentan
Robust, late autumn and winter leek which, provided it is not harvested too late, will yield a heavy crop. Strong stem, 20-30 cm. long. (Bakk)
  Bakk; OGC; Suff

Carina
Developed from our Catalina, it has a longer white shaft and is fit for use from Christmas onwards. Upright leaves do not collect dirt as much as older varieties. (Mars)
  Bree; Mars

Castlestar
  SbS

Catalina
Very productive, giving large crops of long, heavy, non-bulbing leeks. (Foth)
  Dob; SbS; Unwi

Cobham Empire see Yates Empire
Coloma
  SbS

Leek

Cortina
Combining exceptional winter hardiness and long standing ability with sturdy medium length stems, a pure white shaft and dark green leaves. Probably the best late. Maturing January to April. (T&M)
> BREE; JOHN; SBS; T&M

Derrick
Thick, medium length stem with dark, bluish-green foliage. Autumn to early winter use. (EWK)
> EWK; JOHN; SBS; VANH

Elephant
A true autumn leek, early-maturing. It has a short, thick stem which ensures an extremely high yield. Elephant will tolerate some frost without causing any problems. It is, however, advisable not to wait that long and to harvest before the frost sets in. (Bakk)
> BAKK; SBS

Elina
> SBS; YATE

Emperor
> TOZE

Gennevilliers Splendid see Splendid
Giant Winter
> ROG

Giant Winter see Giant Winter 3
Giant Winter 3
Excellent late variety with good length stems. Slow to bolt. (EWK)
> BAKK; CGAR; D&D; EWK; MOLE; OGC; SBS; SMM; WALL; YATE

Giant Winter Granada
> TOZE

Glorina
> BREE

Goldina
> JOHN; YATE

Goliath
A quality autumn maturing variety with a good blanch. (Brwn)
> CGAR; JOHN; JWB; SBS; SMM; TOZE; TUCK; YATE

Hannaball
> SBS

Herfstreuzen see Goliath
Highland Giant
Hardy variety for lifting in January. Long shanks of pure white and will reach a good size when sown late March/early April. (VanH)
VANH

Hiverbleu see Libertas
Jolant
A very vigorous grower for autumn harvesting the shaft is very long with abundant green foliage. No bulbing at the base. Probably the largest and most popular one year growing leek on the market. (VanH)
MOLE; SBS; VANH

Kajak
Long standing winter variety. Dark green foliage and very long white shaft. Has resistance to virus and leaf spot. (EWK)
CGAR; D&D; EWK; OGC; ROG; SBS; SUFF; TUCK

Kelvedon King
SBS

Kilima
RSLU; SBS

King Richard
Very early with extremely long shafts. For late summer and early autumn harvest, though will stand some frost. Maturity 75 days. (OGC)
DOB; JOHN; MARS; OGC; SBS; SUFF; SUTT; T&M; UNWI; YATE

Latina
BREE

Lavi
SBS; YATE

Libertas
A heavy cropping variety that is extremely hardy. White stem. Can be harvested until spring. (Bakk)
BAKK

Longbow
TOZE

Longina
BREE; SBS; WALL

Leek

Longstanton see Odin

Lyon
Good all round variety for autumn use. (EWK)
D&D; EWK; FOTH; JOHN; JWB; MAS; OGC; ROG; SBS; SMM; SUTT; T&M; VANH; WALL

Malabar
SBS

Malabare see Malabar

Mammoth Blanch
A superior exhibition variety with extra long blanch. Specimens grown by amateurs have attained over 5 lbs weight and 100 cu. ins. Exceptionally thick with broad flag. (Rob)
CGAR; JWB; ROB; WALL

Mammoth Pot
A true Pot leek, very thick, with short blanch of approximately 5.5 ins. (13 cms) Bred for the exhibitor but yet retaining good flavour with tight flesh. One of the easiest leeks to grow, very frost hardy. (Rob)
CGAR; ROB; WALL

Marina
BREE

Monstuoso di Carentan see Carentan

Musselburgh
(1822) Harvest December-April. A most reliable and versatile variety which has been justifiably popular for many years. (OGC)
BRWN; CART; CGAR; CHIL; D&D; DOB; EWK; FOTH; JOHN; JWB; MARS; MAS; MOLE; OGC; ROG; SBS; SMM; SUTT; T&M; TUCK; UNWI; VANH; WALL

Odin Longstanton
SBS

Pancho
Early maturing, yet will stand into mid-winter. Long, crisp, white blanched stems of excellent flavour. Ideal for slicing in late salads, or for conventional cooking. (Dob)
DOB; TOZE

Pot
A real exhibition strain. With careful attention will grow to an immense size. (EWK)
EWK; JWB; ROG; SMM; VANH

Prelina
BREE

Prenora
> SBS; YATE

Prizetaker see Lyon
Profina
> BREE

Siegfried Frost
> YATE

Snowstar
First class to eat and to exhibit. Thick, sturdy white stems will hold in excellent condition all winter. A superb strain. (Foth)
> DOB; FOTH; JOHN; SBS; TOZE

Snowstar B
> MOLE; SBS

Splendid
An excellent autumn and early winter leek that does not bulb at the base. It produces uniform blanched shafts about 12 cm. (5 in.) long, 2. 5 cm. (1 in.) diameter. (Unwi)
> JOHN; SBS; SUFF; TOZE; UNWI

St Victor see Blue Solaise
Startrack
A fairly long, slender variety, recommended for early autumn cultivation. Of all Autumn Giant selections Startrack has the darkest leaves. (Bakk)
> BAKK; BRWN; JOHN; TOZE

Sterna
This is an early variety suitable for lifting August/September. A Blue Green Autumn type with strong erect leaves and white stem. 22-24 cm. (Brwn)
> BRWN

Swiss Giant Tilna
> BREE; SBS; TOZE

Tadorna
> MOLE

The Lyon see Lyon
Thor
Early type with very long shafts and medium green foliage. (EWK)
> SBS

Leek

Titan
An early summer leek, forming long stems. However, Titan does not tolerate frost.
This variety has a very agreeable, aromatic flavour. (Bakk)
 BAKK; SBS

Toledo
A significant improvement in late leeks, the stem is almost twice the length of
some varieties. An excellent cropper with winter hardiness for cropping from late
December through to May. (T&M)
 T&M; TOZE

Tropita
Late summer and early autumn variety. Extremely long shanks. (EWK)
 EWK; SBS; SMM

Varna
 RSLU

Verina
Autumn Mammoth type. Strong resistance to rust disease, suited to organic meth-
ods. Produces medium length, very straight leeks with dark green leaves. (Unwi)
 BREE; SBS; UNWI

Walton Mammoth see Autumn Mammoth 2
Wila
An extremely hardy leek with dark blue-green leaves. Stems straight and thick,
increasing in weight in late winter and remaining in condition until May. (Mars)
 MARS

Winora
 YATE

Winter
A fine growing trench leek, very dark green leaves, frost hardy. (Rob)
 ROB

Winter Crop
Outstanding late-maturing, extra-hardy variety with large white stems and very
dark foliage. Stands well for use until April. (Sutt)
 SUTT

Winterreuzen see Giant Winter 3
Wintra
Excellent late winter type for maturity into March. Dark green, strong foliage and
long, white stems. (Suff)
 EWK; SUFF

Yates Empire
A very good leek with thick stems. Matures late, standing well into April. (Unwi)
SBS; UNWI

Leek Other
Allium sp
Elephant Garlic
FUTU

Lettuce
Lactuca sativa
Generally divided into three main categories, Cos, Head and Leaf.

Action
FOTH; WALL

Ambassador
SBS

Bambi
A small cos type, very like Little Gem but with more compact darker green leaves forming a very uniform head approx. 6ins. across. Can also be sown under glass for early crops. (Foth)
FOTH

Bastion
A new crisp head variety for greenhouse production during the winter months. Forms large firm hearts which are welcome as an additional fresh vegetable for Christmas salads. (John)
JOHN; TOZE

Batavia Blonde see Favourite
Besson
BAKK

Blonde de Paris see Favourite
Clarisse
JOHN; TOZE

Cosmic
TOZE

Diana
TOZE

Lettuce

Dynasty
An autumn sowing variety for harvesting up to November/December with uniform habit and attractive heads. Resistant to mosaic virus, downy mildew and a high tolerance of tip burn. (OGC)
> D&D; EWK; OGC

Favourite
> BAKK; SBS

Feltham King
> SBS

Gloire de Nantes see Feltham King

Hudson
> MOLE; SBS

Karlo
> TOZE

Kelly's
A crisp variety with bright green leaves. Sow Oct/Nov for harvest in Mar/Apr. (OGC)
> BRWN; EWK; JOHN; MARS; MOLE; OGC; ROG; SBS; SUFF; TUCK; UNWI; WALL

Kim
> TOZE

Kirsten
> TOZE

Mayfair
May King type. (Brwn)
> TOZE

Pascal
For autumn, winter and spring cutting. Quick growing, thick leaves. Performed among the best in many international trials. Resistant to Bremia races 1, 2, 3, 4, 5 and 6. (Brwn)
> MOLE; SBS

Pavane
A little Gem or "Sucrine" type. Pavane forms a small cos-like head with a dense heart. Slightly darker than Little Gem, Pavane is a very uniform variety with added LMV resistance. (Bree)
> BREE

Perlane
> SBS

Prestine
  SBS

Ravel
Emerald green heads for glasshouse use from October to early May. (EWK)
  EWK; MOLE; SBS

Renania
Forms a robust, tender head which is very slow to run to seed. A true summer lettuce, deservedly called "the pride of every good gardener". (Bakk)
  BAKK

Sangria
  SUTT

Sioux
A new breeding development brings this superb, colourful item to our summer salads. It has deep red outer leaves, but a firm crunchy, blanched heart. Tolerates hot conditions particularly well. (Dob)
  DOB

Zodiac
  CART; JOHN; MOLE; SBS; WALL

Lettuce Cos

Angela
Just as sweet and tender as Little Gem but much easier to separate leaves for garnish, salads etc. Mildew resistant. Virus tolerant. (T&M)
  BREE

Ballon see Balloon

Balloon
A heavy weight cos, light green with a brown tinge to the leaves. (OGC)
  CGAR; EWK; JWB; OGC; SBS

Blonde Maraichere see Paris White

Bubbles
An excellent Little Gem type with very crinkly leaves which snap crisply and have the same superb flavour. Grow at high density. Small gardens. (T&M)
  DOB; MOLE; T&M; TOZE

Carten
  SBS

Corsair
Flat dark green leaves with strong flavour. (SMM)
  DOB; T&M; TOZE

Corsaro
RSLU

Craquerelle du Midi see Winter Density

Dark Green Boston
SBS

Dark Green Cos
Darker green and slower growing than Lobjoits, it is outstanding in later summer crops and is very resistant to tipburn and bolting. LMV tolerant. (Bree)
BREE; JWB; SBS

Grise Maraichere see Lobjoits Green Cos

Jewel
Solid dark heart like a larger Little Gem. Very sweet flavour. Sow spring or autumn. (Mars)
SUTT; TOZE

Little Gem
A cross between cos and cabbage lettuce with some of the benefits of both. Can be sown in the open throughout the growing season and lends itself well to being sown in the early autumn and cloched during the winter. (OGC)
BREE; BRWN; CART; CGAR; D&D; DOB; EWK; FOTH; JOHN; JWB; MARS; MOLE; OGC; ROG; RSLU; SBS; SMM; SUFF; SUTT; T&M; TOZE; TUCK; UNWI; VANH; WALL; YATE

Lobjoits Green Cos
Tall, deep green hearts, very crisp. Self-folding. (Mars)
BREE; BRWN; D&D; EWK; FOTH; JOHN; JWB; MARS; MOLE; OGC; ROG; SBS; SUFF; SUTT; TOZE; TUCK; VANH; WALL; YATE

Paris Island cos
SBS

Paris White
Much improved cos type with medium large compact heads. Will stand for a long time when ready to cut. (EWK)
CART; CHIL; D&D; EWK; JWB; ROG; SBS; WALL

Romance
Makes a substantial, tightly folded head with crisp, sweet heart. (Dob)
BREE; DOB

Rossalita
A new red cos or romaine from the US. Medium sized with purple-red outer leaf colour and emerald green base. The heart blanches yellow. Excellent flavour and crisp texture. Earlier than most cos and suitable for spring and autumn cropping. (Suff)
> BREE; SUFF

Rouge d'Hiver
A good tasty cos with long red pointed leaves. Very hardy. Sow late summer/autumn or early spring. An old French variety and very rare. (Suff)
> SUFF

Sucrine see Little Gem
Toledo
Half way between Little Gem and a standard cos. Dark green leaves give a very sweet flavour and no bitterness. Mini cos. Reliable. Virus tolerant. (T&M)
> RSLU; T&M

Val d'Orge see Valdor
Valdor
Overwinter greenhouse type. This can also be sown outside. Attractive light green heads with good resistance to bolting. Sow in Aug/Sep. (OGC)
> CART; CGAR; DOB; EWK; JWB; MOLE; OGC; ROG; SBS; SMM; SUTT; TUCK; WALL

Valmaine
A cos type used for cut and come again, giving two crops from one sowing. Very productive and the individual leaves are deliciously crisp. Resistant to some races of mildew and particularly useful for summer/autumn use. (OGC)
> EWK; JOHN; JWB; MOLE; OGC; SBS; TOZE; YATE

Vaux's Self Folding
> JOHN

Winter Density
Larger than Little Gem; a very good crisp variety, much used for autumn sowing. (OGC)
> BRWN; CGAR; CHIL; D&D; DOB; EWK; FOTH; JOHN; JWB; MARS; MOLE; OGC; ROG; SBS; SUTT; TOZE; UNWI; VANH; WALL

Lettuce Head
All The Year Round
(1831) A butterhead type for successional sowings from spring to autumn. (OGC) CART; CGAR; CHIL; DOB; EWK; FOTH; JOHN; JWB; MARS; OGC; ROG; SBS; SMM; SUTT; T&M; TUCK; UNWI; WALL

Animo
JOHN

Arctic King
Very hardy variety for autumn sowing outside to cut early spring. (EWK) CGAR; D&D; EWK; JOHN; JWB; MAS; ROG; SBS; SUTT; TUCK; VANH; WALL

Attraction see Unrivalled
Aubade
JOHN

Avoncrisp
A crisp head type for autumn harvest. It can also be used for "cut-and-come-again" cropping. (OGC) CGAR; EWK; JWB; MARS; MOLE; OGC; ROG; SBS; TUCK; WALL; YATE

Avondefiance
Dark green in colour. Useful for summer sowing due to its high resistance to mildew. Popular with commercial growers, and successful in warm climates. (OGC) BRWN; CGAR; DOB; EWK; JOHN; JWB; MARS; MOLE; OGC; ROG; SBS; SUTT; TUCK; VANH; WALL; YATE

Baltic
The largest, most solid iceberg, providing crisp, succulent salads from June onwards. In our trials it proved more resistant to cool spring weather than Saladin, which it replaces. (Mars) MARS; RSLU

Beatrice
A new generation of lettuce. Early, easy to grow with excellent mildew and root aphid resistance, superb vigour and fast crop growth. Ideal as an early Iceberg, with bright green solid crunchy heads and short internal stalk. (T&M) MOLE; T&M

Bellona
YATE

Berlo
TOZE

Blonde a Bord Rouge see Iceberg

Borough Wonder
Excellent summer variety for a regular sowing. Large, pale green, tender heads. (EWK)
> CGar; EWK; John; Rog; Wall

Bristol
> John

British Hilde see Hilde II

Bruna di Germania
Small red/brown hardy lettuce for overwintering, growing to 8 in. Does better with some protection, i. e. a cold frame, or tunnel. (Suff)
> Suff

Burgundy Boston
> SbS; SMM

Buttercrunch
Dark green with compact heads which stands well. The central leaves are very crisp and it is resistant to hot weather. One of the best garden lettuces. (OGC)
> Brwn; CGar; D&D; Dob; EWK; Foth; John; JWB; OGC; Rog; SbS; Suff; T&M; Unwi; VanH; Wall

Capitol
The best Iceberg for spring cropping in the cold greenhouse. Firm, heavy, crisp and crunchy heads. (T&M)
> T&M; Toze

Carlton
> John

Chaperon
This slow-bolting butterhead type is suitable for spring, summer and early autumn crops. Has a nice heart with yellow-green leaves, strongly tinged with red outer leaves. Large heads. (Brwn)
> Brwn; John

Cindy
> Mole; Wall

Claret
> John

Clarion
Thick leaved variety cropping throughout the summer. Bremia resistant. (EWK)
> Brwn; EWK; John; Mole; SbS; Toze

Cobham Green
Similar to New Market, but dark green colour. (JWB)
> JOHN; JWB; MOLE; SBS; TOZE; WALL

Columbus
Greenhouse type. Fast growing. Bright green thick textured leaves. Sow late August to mid-February for late October-early May cropping. (Dob)
> CART; CGAR; DOB; EWK; SBS

Constant Heart see Hilde II
Continuity
Only suitable for sowing in the spring and summer, it is very long standing. Distinct reddish brown in colour, it improves the appearance of a mixed salad. It is claimed that the colour deters pigeons. (OGC)
> CGAR; EWK; JOHN; JWB; OGC; ROG; SBS; TUCK; WALL

Cortina
> JOHN

Crestana
Crisp dense heads, like supermarket icebergs but much greener. Tolerates wide range of conditions. Very reliable. Mildew resistant. Virus tolerant. (T&M)
> BREE; T&M

Crispino
> RSLU

Cynthia
A crisp, tasty butterhead type that is a little later to harvest than Kwiek. (Foth)
> SBS; UNWI

Dandie
Autumn sowing, glasshouse variety for cutting March and April. Well filled heads of good colour. (EWK)
> CGAR; SBS; WALL

Daphne
> MOLE; SBS; TOZE; WALL; YATE

De Verrieres see Imperial Winter
Debby
Extremely versatile. It can be sown indoors from January, outdoors from March to late July, to crop from May until early November. It is noted for producing full, firm heads in mid-summer, when many other varieties bolt easily. Resistance to lettuce root aphid, mildew and lettuce mosaic virus. (Mars)
> MARS; UNWI

Delta
SBS

Dolly
A large, dark green, butterhead variety suitable for growing in a cold or slightly heated greenhouse. Sow from October-January for February-April harvesting. Resistant to mildew and tipburn. (Sutt)
UNWI

E6400
YATE

El Toro
Hard, dense, crisp, crunchy head. Very quick growing, yet mature heads stand till October. (T&M)
JOHN; T&M

Fivia
Firm, crisp, heavy heads with an attractive pink tinge. Sow mid-September to mid-January, harvest early November to late March. (T&M)
T&M

Fortune see Hilde II
Grande
RSLU

Great Lakes see Great Lakes 659
Great Lakes 659
The well-known American crisphead lettuce which forms a real "cabbage" that is not prone to bolt. Can be kept in the refrigerator for quite some time. (Bakk)
BAKK; BRWN; CGAR; EWK; JOHN; JWB; MARS; MAS; MOLE; OGC; SBS; SMM; UNWI; WALL

Great Lakes Mesa 659
SBS

Grosse Blonde Paresseuse
A slow-bolting summer lettuce producing large, light green heads. (Bakk)
BAKK

Hilde II
Is at present considered one of the most cultivated varieties. Produces solid, healthy heads, tender and with a very fine flavour. Recommended! (Bakk)
BAKK; CART; MARS; SBS; SUTT; UNWI; VANH

Lettuce Head

Iceberg
This is essentially a summer lettuce with pale green leaves, slightly red tinged with large crisp white hearts. (OGC)
CGAR; EWK; JOHN; JWB; MOLE; OGC; ROG; SBS; SMM; SUFF; T&M; TUCK; VANH; WALL

Impala
Impala is a short day lettuce, producing high quality heads with a well closed base. Suggested sowing period September to November. Optimum harvest period December-April. Bremia resistance. (RSlu)
JOHN; SBS; YATE

Imperial Winter
A hardy outdoor variety for autumn sowing and cutting in the spring. (OGC)
BAKK; BRWN; CGAR; EWK; JOHN; OGC; ROG; SBS; WALL

Ithaca
A crisp variety, slow bolting, resistant against mildew and tipburn. (Mole)
MOLE; SBS; TOZE

Jarino
BAKK

Kagraner Sommer see Standwell

Kares
A really excellent variety for mid-summer to early autumn use. Excellent dark green lettuce, resistant to almost all diseases, and slow to bolt. Sow from March onwards. (VanH)
VANH

Kelvin
JOHN; MOLE; RSLU; SBS; WALL

King Crown
Superb thick, dark green leaves and large solid heads. Suitable for spring, late summer and autumn sowing and does well in all soils. (EWK)
EWK; SBS

Kloek
A butterhead type for overwintering. Sow Oct/Nov for harvest in Mar/Apr. (OGC)
CGAR; D&D; EWK; OGC; ROG; SBS; WALL

Kwiek
A butterhead variety for cutting in Nov/Dec. Sow in late August. (OGC)
CGAR; D&D; EWK; JOHN; JWB; OGC; ROG; SBS; SUFF; SUTT; VANH; WALL

Kylie
BREE

Lake Nyah
A very uniform bright green crisp lettuce of good quality, especially recommended for July and August cutting when well developed medium-sized hearts will be produced. Stands well and is a fine variety of the Iceberg type. (Sutt)
CGᴀʀ; SʙS

Lakeland
The best iceberg lettuce for spring, summer or autumn. It comes into cut earlier than most and is ideal for spring cropping in frames as well as outdoor. It is resistant to mildew and lettuce root aphid. (Mars)
Bʀᴡɴ; Cᴀʀᴛ; Dᴏʙ; Fᴏᴛʜ; Mᴀʀs; Tᴏᴢᴇ; Uɴᴡɪ

Lilian
Firm, well-wrapped heads of bright green with generous hearts of crisp-sweet taste. Ideal for successional sowings either in the open or under cloches. (Dob)
Dᴏʙ; Tᴏᴢᴇ

Lollo Rosso
CGᴀʀ

Maikonig see May King
Malika
Outdoor crisp lettuce valued for its earliness, unlike some other early varieties, "coning" in Malika is virtually unknown. Performs very well from early production under polythene as well as from unprotected crops. LMV tolerant. (Bree)
Bʀᴇᴇ; Jᴏʜɴ; SʙS; Uɴᴡɪ

Marmer
Very firm, crisp, heavy heads. Sow Aug/Sep, harvest January. Sow Nov/Jan, harvest April on. Grows best in cool conditions. (T&M)
SʙS

Marshall
Large iceberg type lettuces with full heads and slightly bubbled, succulent leaves. (Foth)
Yᴀᴛᴇ

Massa
SʙS

May King
An autumn planting lettuce, it can be equally successful when planted in the spring or summer. Mid-green, slightly tinged with red, early and hardy, it is first class for frame, cold greenhouse or outdoor growing. (OGC)
Bᴀᴋᴋ; Dᴏʙ; EWK; JWB; SʙS

May Queen see May King

Meraviglia delle Quattro Stagioni see Merveille des Quatre Saisons

Merveille Des Quatre Saisons

The variety can be grown all year through but is best from spring and autumn sowing. Good solid heads with large curled, red leaves of fine flavour. (EWK)

> BREE; EWK; JOHN; MOLE; OGC; SBS; SMM; SUFF; TOZE; WALL

Merveille d'Hiver see Imperial Winter

Michelle

> YATE

Minetto

> SBS

Mirian

> BREE

Musette

An excellent mid-green variety for summer and autumn, Musette is uniform with a large head. It shows resistance to downy mildew and mosaic virus. (OGC)

> JOHN; MOLE; OGC; SBS; SUTT; TUCK

Nancy

> MOLE

Neckarriesen

Produces tender, large, bright green heads. A top quality lettuce with an excellent flavour, suitable for spring and summer cultivation. The seed is virus-free, so it will give an extremely high yield. (Bakk)

> BAKK

New Market see Unrivalled

New York see Webbs Wonderful

Novita

Curly lettuce with a very well-filled head. Crispy texture and special flavour. Easier to grow than other varieties because of its resistance to tipburn. For sowing from September to mid-February. (Mars)

> BRWN; EWK; MARS; OGC; ROG; SBS; SUFF; TUCK

Oresto

> RSLU

Oxford

> JOHN

Pandorian

> BREE

Pantra
> BREE

Parella
One of the hardiest winter lettuces grown in the mountainous region of Northern Italy. Survived -15 degrees C in a cold winter. Broadcast autumn or spring and thin to 4-6 in. apart. Very tiny neat lettuce forming small heart or rosette. Cut and come again or harvest whole plant. (Suff)
> SUFF

Parella Red
A decorative red version of the compact and hardy Parella Green. When left to bolt it makes a most decorative plant good enough for the flower garden. (Suff)
> SUFF

Paulette
> JOHN

Pennlake
Crinkly leaved, maturing just after Avoncrisp. A first class market variety. (Brwn)
> BRWN; JOHN; MOLE; SBS; YATE

Plena see Hilde II

Plevanos
> SBS

Poulton Market see Hilde II

Prior
> JOHN

Rachel
A semi-thick leaved variety with fresh green leaves, the heart is open and well filled, with a strong flat base. Sow August-December to cut throughout the winter. (Brwn)
> BRWN; JOHN; MOLE

Rebecca
> JOHN; MOLE; WALL

Red Fire
Highly frilled dard red leaves. Heads have good uniformity and excellent flavour. Cropping from summer to autumn. Slow to bolt. (EWK)
> CGAR; EWK; SBS; SMM

Lettuce Head

Red Valeria
The most intense red with a uniform mound of fine serrated loose leaves. The centre can become slightly green/blonde. Looks so attractive and tastes quite exceptional. (Foth)
FOTH

Regina dei Ghiacci
Crisphead lettuce for summer use; slow to run to seed. Sow March to July, thinning to 8-10 ins apart. Attractive foliage. (Suff)
SUFF

Reskia
The variety for all season cropping from spring to autumn. Butterhead type with firm, large mid-green heads. (EWK)
EWK; JOHN; JWB; MOLE; ROG; VANH; WALL

Ricardo
Short day cultivar for unheated or heated greenhouse. Thick leaved butterhead setting new standards for this type of lettuce. (Tuck)
JOHN; SBS; TUCK

Ritmo
YATE

Rosana
JOHN; MOLE; TOZE

Rossa Fruilana
Forms an attractive frilly leaved red tinged heart. Most decorative in summer salads. Like many lettuce varieties it will resprout from its base if cut young. (Suff)
SUFF

Rossimo
This is between a crisp and a butterhead variety, lightly savoyed with curled margins, round to flat crisp leaves. Perfect for modern salad bowls. (Foth)
FOTH

Rouge Grenobloise
Crisp, heavy lettuce with a very pleasant flavour. Hardly or not at all bolting and, therefore, very suitable for sowing in summer. (Bakk)
BAKK

Rougette du Midi
A most attractive small reddish leaved lettuce. Sow in autumn for winter and spring lettuce. Very crisp and tasty. (Suff)
SUFF

Ruth
This variety has a glossy dark green leaf with slightly upright growth and good heart filling with clean flat base. Bremia NL 1-15 resistant. Sow August-December to cut throughout the winter. (Brwn)
BRWN; JOHN

Sabrina
An excellent addition to your choice of lettuce for the winter months. Inspire your salad bowl with the mouth watering, fresh green leaves and crisp heart. It grows fast, autumn to spring, in a slightly heated or unheated greenhouse. Good disease resistance. (Foth)
FOTH; MOLE; TOZE; YATE

Saladin
An excellent crisphead variety, producing solid iceberg type heads, light green in colour. Slow to bolt in hot weather and useful throughout the spring and summer. (OGC)
BAKK; BREE; BRWN; CGAR; CHIL; D&D; DOB; EWK; FOTH; JOHN; JWB; MOLE; OGC; ROG; RSLU; SBS; TOZE; TUCK; UNWI; VANH; YATE

Salina
Mid green butterhead variety for summer production or protected cropping under polythene/glass. (CGar)
MOLE; SBS

Sigmaball
Large, round, mid-green hearts of slightly crisp texture and fine flavour. Stands in condition over a long period, and is resistant to tipburn and root aphid. Sow outdoors April-June in succession. (Sutt)
SUTT

Sitonia
For harvesting late spring, summer and autumn. Excellent resistance to tipburn and bolting. Resistant to Bremia. (Brwn)
MOLE; SBS

Soraya
JOHN

Standwell
BAKK

Supermarket see Hilde II
Suzan
Soft butterhead type with good compact heads. Quick maturity for early summer use. (EWK)
BRWN; CGAR; EWK; JOHN; JWB; MOLE; ROG; SBS; SUTT; TUCK; WALL

Lettuce Head

Tanja
JOHN

Target
SUTT; YATE

Telda
RSLU

Tiger
Distinctive in the garden and on the plate. The deep red outer leaves surround pale green tender hearts, which are extremely heavy. Their flavour was better than all other icebergs. (Mars)
MARS

Timo
YATE

Titania
JOHN; MOLE; TOZE; YATE

Tom Thumb
An early dwarf variety which deserves greater popularity. It hearts quickly and is compact and long standing, thus cutting down on wastage. (OGC)
BRWN; CART; CGAR; CHIL; DOB; EWK; FOTH; JOHN; JWB; MARS; MOLE; OGC; ROG; SBS; SUFF; SUTT; T&M; TUCK; UNWI; WALL

Trocadero Improved see Unrivalled

Unrivalled
Medium-sized hearts. Sow outdoors in spring and summer. Also excellent for January-February sowing under glass for transplanting outdoors. (Sutt)
CHIL; EWK; EWK; JOHN; JWB; MOLE; OGC; ROG; SBS; SUTT; WALL

Vicky
JOHN; MOLE; TOZE; YATE

Virginia
TOZE

Warpath
Bred in England. A cross between a cos and an Iceberg with eating qualities from both and the crunchy leaves form a small heart. Faster to mature than an Iceberg it can be sown at up to twice the density. It has good bolt resistance. (Foth)
BRWN; FOTH; SUTT

Webbs Wonderful
One of the most popular of all lettuces, crisp, solid, large, long standing and of excellent quality. (OGC)
> CART; CGAR; CHIL; D&D; DOB; EWK; FOTH; JOHN; JWB; MARS; MOLE; OGC; ROG; SBS; SMM; SUFF; SUTT; T&M; TUCK; UNWI; VANH; WALL

Windermere
An outstanding quality crisphead. Medium sized heads, very uniform growth. (OGC)
> CGAR; EWK; JWB; OGC; ROG; SBS; SUTT; WALL

Winter Crop see Imperial Winter
Winter Marvel see Imperial Winter

Lettuce Leaf

Americana Bruna
> BAKK

Bataser
> BREE

Biscia Rossa
A very pretty lettuce with red tinged leaves from Italy. May be used for cut and come again or allowed to grow on. (Suff)
> SUFF

Canasta
> BREE; JOHN

Carnival
A loose leaf lettuce which forms large heads but does not heart. Glossy green leaves with a rosy tinge. Super crisp leaf. (OGC)
> SUTT

Catalogna
(Radichetta) Something quite new from Italy. A cut and come again lettuce for all seasons. Leaves are elongated and deeply lobed, light green with tender crunchy ribs. Very fast regrowing. (Suff)
> SUFF

Cocarde
A large red oakleaf of the arrowhead type from France. Heads are trumpet shaped and leaves dark green with a red overlay. Superb salad quality. Slow bolting. 49 Days. (Suff)
> SUFF

Doree de Printemps see Bataser

Everest
JOHN

Grand Rapids
SBS

Little Leprechaun
A striking red-leaved semi-cos type. Very compact with good tolerance to heat and bolting. (OGC)
EWK; OGC; SUFF

Lollo Bianda Casablanca
RSLU

Lollo Bionda
The fresh green cousin of Lollo Rossa. (Mars)
BREE; DOB; EWK; MARS; MOLE; SBS; T&M; TOZE; WALL; YATE

Lollo Green
Unlike any zucchini you have ever seen. Fruits grow long and curved with a bell at the flower end. Harvest fruits at around 30 cm. long. Fruits will grow to a spectacular metre long and they are still good to eat. Plants are very vigorous climbers or can trail on the ground. (Suff)
SUFF

Lollo Mixed
A delightful and attractive mixture of the popular Italian Lollo type lettuce, including the bright green Lollo Verde, with Rossa for extra colour in salads and garnishes. (Unwi)
UNWI

Lollo Red see Lollo Rosso

Lollo Rossa
A deliciously crips lettuce with frilly leaves tinged with red. Decorative enough to include in the flower garden! (OGC)
BAKK; BREE; CART; CGAR; CHIL; DOB; EWK; FOTH; JOHN; JWB; MARS; MOLE; OGC; SBS; SMM; SUFF; SUTT; T&M; TOZE; TUCK; UNWI; VANH; WALL

Lollo Rossa Astina
JOHN; RSLU

Lollo Rossa Lovina
YATE

Lumina
Lumina produces loose, open-leaved plants that allow you to either cut the whole plant for use in one go, or to pick the outer leaves and return for more as you need them. The rich red and green leaves protect the paler green, crispy heart. (Unwi)
UNWI

Pablo
Provides a real lift to salads. The medium heads have thick, smooth leaves with true iceberg crispness, flavour and an attractive outer red sheen. (Foth)
FOTH; JOHN; RSLU; T&M

Raisa
Two for the price of one. The young plants provide deep red oak leaves for garnish; more mature plants have a densly filled centre, tender and juicy, for the salad bowl. Each sowing will give you a supply for weeks. (Mars)
MARS

Red Sails
Distinct All-American Selection winner. Highly recommended and nutritional, it is a loose leaf type and, with a greater leaf area exposed to the sun, has six times the vitamin A than of other crisp head varieties. The bronzy-red leaves greatly enhance a salad. (John)
JOHN

Riccia a folglia di Quercia
Oak leaved lettuce for cutting. Use for cut and come again crop. Sow broadcast from spring to autumn. Cut young leaves when about 2 in. high, leaving plant to resprout. (Suff)
SUFF

Rusty
TOZE

Salad Bowl
A very useful lettuce quite different from other varieties, as it has no heart, and a few leaves can be taken without uprooting the whole plant. (OGC)
CART; CGAR; D&D; DOB; EWK; JOHN; JWB; MARS; OGC; ROG; SBS; SUFF; SUTT; TUCK; VANH; WALL

Salad Bowl Greenwich
BREE

Salad Bowl Mixed
Both the colours of oak-leaf lettuce together, with this crisp and tender non-hearting variety. Leaves can be picked a few at a time. Hardly ever bolts. (Foth)
FOTH; UNWI

Salad Bowl Red
A pretty form of Salad Bowl Green. Ideal for small gardens, will last throughout the summer if picked regularly. (Suff)
> BAKK; BRWN; CGAR; D&D; DOB; EWK; JOHN; JWB; MOLE; OGC; ROG; SBS; SUFF; SUTT; TOZE; TUCK; VANH; WALL

Salad Bowl Red Kamino
Similar plant type to Salad Bowl, with indented oak leaf but with strong red coloration. Suitable for outdoor cropping in spring, summer and autumn. (Bree)
> BREE

Salad Bowl Red Rebosa
> RSLU

Salad Bowl Red Selma
> YATE

Sigla
A very attractive frilled leaf type with intense deep red colour. Low nitrate content. For spring, summer and early autumn cropping, also highly recommended for glasshouse crops. (Brwn)
> BRWN; MOLE

Soprane
> YATE

Valeria
This versatile variety, is a counterpart of Lollo Rossa and Lollo Bionda, producing intensive red leaf colour when grown during the winter months in a frost-free greenhouse or frame. Also superb when grown outdoors during spring and summer. (Dob)
> DOB

Lettuce Stem

Lactuca sativa var. augustana
Celtuce is one name given to this variety of lettuce, grown for the swollen stem.

Celtuce
Halfway between celery and lettuce, the stems and leaves are excellent alternatives and very tasty. (Foth). Celtuce is not a cross, but a type of lettuce grown primarily for its swollen stem.
> CGAR; CHAM; CHIL; EWK; JWB; OGC; SBS; SMM; SUTT; T&M; VANH; WALL

Woh Sun
Grown for centuries in China. The leaves are used as lettuce, or in stir-fry and the stem for Shanghai pickles. Try the heart of the stem in salads. Has a faint lettuce flavour and an unusually juicy and crisp texture. (Suff)

SUFF

Lettuce Thai
Thai Lettuce
OGC; SUFF

Litchi Tomato
Solanum sisymbriifolium

An unusual and attractive tomato-like plant with divided leaves and spines on stems and leaves. Bluish-white flowers produce cherry-sized red fruit which are comparable in flavour to the tropical litchi fruit. They are eaten raw or in preserves. Needs a warm sunny position outside, or can be easily grown in a greenhouse.

Litchi Tomato
FUTU

Mangel
Beta vulgaris
Brooks Red Intermediate
A fast disappearing product, ideal winter food for ponies, horses and wine making. (JWB)

JWB

Prizewinner
Large golden orange roots which are ideal for wine making. Can also be used for feeding to goats. Very easy to grow. (EWK)

EWK; OGC; ROG; SBS; SUFF; WALL

Wintergold
SBS

Marrow
Cucurbita pepo

There is much confusion over marrows, squashes, and courgettes, or zucchini. All these marrows can be picked small as courgettes.

Marrow

F1 Acceste
RSlu; T&M

All Green Bush
Popular and reliable. A heavy cropper if kept picked. Do not allow the fruit to grow beyond 6 in. (D&D)
Chil; D&D; EWK; Foth; John; JWB; Mole; OGC; Rog; SbS; SMM; Unwi; VanH; Wall

F1 Altea
Bree

F1 Ambassador
CGar; Dob; EWK; Foth; John; Mars; Mole; OGC; RSlu; SbS; Toze; Tuck; Yate

F1 Arlesa
Bree

Bianco Friulano
Rated top class. Produces a good crop of crook necked squash which are pale yellow in colour with a warty appearance. Delicious flavour and firm texture. Cook the same as zucchini. (Suff)
OGC; Suff

Brimmer
Rated the best open pollinated variety in National Trials. Pick regularly for lots of high quality, succulent and tasty courgettes. An off shoot of hybrid breeding, the colour may vary a little from fruit to fruit. (T&M)
CGar; John; SbS

Burpee Golden Zucchini
CGar; D&D; EWK; OGC; Rog; SbS; Sutt

Bush Green
A popular variety for the small garden. (JWB)
JWB

Bush White
Suitable for the small garden.JWB
JWB

Clarella
A new type of courgette with a remarkable delicate and distinctive flavour. Really delicious. A courgette with a pale green skin and sometimes a slightly flask shaped. A very productive bush variety. Pick the fruits young or leave to grow to small marrow size. (Suff)
OGC; Suff

F1 Clarita
Unwi

Cobham Green Bush
Medium length fruits, medium green in colour with cream yellow stripe. Produces very attractive tasty marrows, quite unlike an overgrown courgette. (Bree)
Toze

F1 Cobra
SBS

F1 Crusader
Brwn

Custard White
An attractive bush variety with round and flattened white fruits about 7 in. in diameter, which have scalloped edges. (Dob)
Brwn; CGar; EWK; John; JWB; Mole; OGC; Rog; SBS; SMM; Suff; Tuck; Wall

Custard Yellow
SBS

F1 Defender
Sutt; Toze

F1 Diamond
Bakk; Mole; SBS

Early Gem see Storr's Green
F1 Elite
John; SBS; Toze

Emerald Cross see Greyzini
F1 Festival
SBS

F1 Gold Rush
Bakk; Bree; Brwn; Chil; Dob; Foth; John; JWB; Mars; Mole; RSlu; SBS; Suff; T&M; Toze; Unwi; Wall; Yate

Golden Zucchini see Burpee Golden
Green Bush see Long Green Bush
Green Bush F1 Hybrid see Storr's Green
Green Bush Improved
Very early-maturing plants producing small, dark green, tender fruits in abundance. (Sutt)
Sutt

Marrow

Green Gem
SbS

Green Trailing see Long Green Trailing

F1 Greyzini
EWK; Mole; Rog; RSlu; SbS; Toze; Tuck; Yate

F1 Jackpot
SbS

Kingsize
For really huge exhibition winning giant marrows or simply to amaze your friends. (T&M)
T&M

Long Green Bush
Probably the most popular - the compact, bushy habit is ideal for the smaller garden. (Foth)
CGar; Chil; D&D; EWK; Foth; John; OGC; Rog; RSlu; SbS; T&M; Tuck; VanH; Wall; Yate

Long Green Bush 2
Dark green marrows with prominent cream stripes. (Mars)
Cart; Dob; Mars; Unwi

Long Green Bush 3 Smallpak
Similar to Green Bush improved, but fruits are shorter. Excellent for exhibition. (Sutt)
Sutt

Long Green Bush 4
Fruit rather smaller than the trailing type, dark green with lighter stripes. (Brwn)
Brwn

Long Green Striped see Long Green Trailing

Long Green Trailing
Large fruits of dark green with paler stripes and a most delicious flesh. Stores well.
(Foth)
CGar; D&D; Dob; EWK; John; JWB; Mars; Mole; OGC; Rog; SbS; Suff;
Sutt; T&M; Tuck; Unwi; VanH; Wall

Long White Bush
Well-known variety, light green in colour and very tasty. If you do not let the fruit
grow too large, you can harvest over a longer period. (Bakk)
Bakk; CGar; Dob; Rog; SbS

Long White Trailing
A very prolific variety with large white fruits. (Dob)
Dob; JWB; SbS

Marco see Ambassador

F1 Market King
EWK; SbS

Minipak
Green striped marrows grow to about 12 in. A very productive bush variety. Firm
fruits of excellent quality. (Suff)
CGar; Chil; EWK; Rog; SbS; SMM; Wall

F1 Moreno
Foth; John; Mars; SbS; Yate

F1 Onyx
SbS

F1 Otaria
SbS

Prepak
SbS

F1 President
John; Mole; SbS; Yate

F1 Raven
Bree; Foth

F1 Saracen
Brwn; Toze

F1 Sardane
T&M

Marrow

F1 Storr's Green
BREE; CART; CGAR; D&D; DOB; EWK; JOHN; JWB; MARS; MOLE; OGC; ROG; SBS; SMM; SUFF; SUTT; TOZE; UNWI; VANH; YATE

F1 Supremo
BREE; DOB; T&M; WALL

Table Dainty
Medium-sized fruits striped pale and dark green. Early maturing, and excellent for exhibition. (Sutt)
JOHN; JWB; SBS; SUTT

F1 Tarmino
UNWI

Tender and True
Round, mottled green fruits from early maturing plants. Ideal for small gardens. (Sutt)
JWB; SUTT

F1 Tiger Cross
FOTH; MOLE; SUTT; T&M; TOZE; WALL

Tondo di Nizza
Round courgette. Very productive, the fruit may be cut from 2-4 in. Ideal for stuffing. (Suff)
SUFF; T&M

Tondo do Nizza
A round Italian variety. Pick when up to 4in in diameter. Ideal for stuffing. (OGC)
OGC

Tondo do Nizza
A round Italian variety. Pick when up to 4in in diameter. Ideal for stuffing. (OGC)

Tromboncino
Unlike any zucchini you have ever seen. Fruits grow long and curved with a bell at the flower end. Harvest fruits at around 30 cm. long. Fruits will grow to a spectacular metre long and they are still good to eat. Plants are very vigorous climbers or can trail on the ground. (Suff)
SUFF

Vegetable Spaghetti
Trailing type which produces oval yellow/white fruit which can be stored in a frost-proof shed. The flesh is stringy, hence the name. (D&D)

BRWN; CGAR; CHIL; D&D; DOB; EWK; JOHN; JWB; OGC; SBS; SMM; SUFF; SUTT; TUCK; VANH; WALL

F1 Zebra Cross
MARS; MOLE; TOZE; YATE

F1 Zucchini
Long, slender, dark green fruits of good flavour. Often used as courgettes when young and tender. (Sutt)

BRWN; EWK; ROG; SUTT; TOZE; WALL

F1 Zucchini Blondy
T&M

Zucchini Dark Green
SBS

Zucchini F1 see Storr's Green
F1 Zucchini Spineless Beauty
T&M

Zucchini True French
Deep green courgette. Constant cutting will ensure a heavy crop. Cook unpeeled, as they have tender skins, and allow to sizzle in butter. (T&M)

T&M

Mashua
Tropaeolum tuberosum
Another Lost Vegetable of the Incas, with gorgeous flowers and edible tubers.

Constanza
A late flowering variety with pale tubers flecked with red. (Futu)

FUTU

Melon

Mashua

A close relative of the naturtium, mashua is cultivated in the Andes for its edible tubers. A climbing perennial up to 2 m. if given support, it will also grow across the ground, forming a dense mass of weed supressing foliage. Attractive orange-red trumpet shaped flowers are borne in the summer and autumn until a hard frost kills the plant. The tubers are about the size of small potatoes and have a yellow skin with numerous purple flecks. Eaten raw, they have a hot, mustardy flavour. This is lost on cooking and a strange, vanilla-like taste takes its place; definitely an acquirted taste. They can be boiled, baked or roasted. Tuberisation occurs as the days become shorter and in areas that have early frosts there may be insufficient time for tubers to develop properly. The plants are known to have nematocidal, bacteriocidal and insecticidal properties and in the Andes they are often intercropped with other tubers such as ocas and potatoes. (Futu)

FUTU; POYN

Melon

Cucumis melo

F1 Amber Nectar
T&M

F1 Ananas
BAKK; CGAR; EWK

F1 Aroma
CGAR; EWK; SBS

Blenheim Orange
Good size fruits with scarlet flesh and lovely flavour. (OGC)
CGAR; D&D; EWK; JWB; OGC; ROG; SBS; SMM; SUTT; UNWI; WALL

Charentais
Juicy, orange flesh from this canteloupe-type. Can be grown in the greenhouse, or under cloches or frames. (Foth)
BRWN; CGAR; FOTH; SBS; TOZE; VANH

F1 Donar
SBS

Dutch Net
Medium size melon, sweet. (CGar)
CGAR

Early Dawn
Hybrid musk melon with good yield and firm good flavoured orange flesh. (Toze)
TOZE

Melon

F1 Early Sweet
> Sutt

Emerald Gem
Rich green flesh of unusual thickness and excellent flavour. (Sutt)
> Sutt

F1 Fiesta
> Yate

F1 Galia
> T&M

Ha'on
> Yate

Hero of Lockinge
Richly flavoured white flesh. For heated or cold greenhouse. (Sutt)
> Sutt

Honey Dew
Also called "white sugar" which is an appropriate name because this delicious melon is extraordinarily sweet. Unsurpassed as a dessert melon. (Bakk)
> Bakk

Jenny Lind
An heirloom melon with very aromatic exquisite flavour. Medium early, medium size fruits. (T&M)
> T&M

Minnesota Midget
Takes up just 3 ft. of space. Each mini-vine grows many orange fleshed, tender to the rind, 4 in. melons with an exceptionally high sugar content and superb flavour. (T&M)
> T&M

No Name
Juicy and aromatic amber-yellow flesh, full of superb flavour. Attractive green and yellow marbled skin. One of the best melons for cropping outdoors. Grow in either the cold greenhouse, frame or under cloches. (Unwi)
> Unwi

Ogen
Rather small, striped green fruits, 4-6 in. across, produced very freely. Sweet, green flesh. (Mars)
> Brwn; CGar; D&D; Dob; EWK; John; JWB; Mars; Mole; Rog; SbS; Sutt; T&M; Toze; Tuck; VanH; Wall

F1 Overgen Panogen
BREE

F1 Romeo
MARS

F1 Summer Dream hybrid
BAKK

F1 Sweetheart
BRWN; CART; CGAR; D&D; DOB; EWK; FOTH; JOHN; JWB; MARS; MOLE;
OGC; ROG; SBS; SUFF; SUTT; T&M; TUCK; UNWI; WALL; YATE

Westlandia Sugar see Honey Dew
Witte Suiker see Honey Dew

Melukhi
Melukhi
Jew's Mallow, or Jute. Not only is this plant an important source of Jute, but it is also a vegetable much grown in Eastern Mediterranean countries, being much esteemed in Egypt. It is a tall, very slender annual plant with toothed leaves and small, axillary, yellow flowers. Malukhi is used in the same way as spinach in chicken soup, as puree or with cheese and flavouring in strudel dough for a delicious pastry boreka. The young leaves can be used in salads when young and tender. Although being a native of hot countries it will probably need a hot summer to succeed well in this country, it nevertheless should be worth a trial as a half-hardy annual. 2-12ft. (Chil)
CHIL

Mesclun
Mixed Salad Leaf
The "green salad" of southern France. Traditionally it contains a minimum of 7 different leaves to which herbs and edible petals are added. (Foth)
FOTH

Mibuna Greens
Related to Mizuna greens, but uncertain.
The latest escapee from behind the bamboo curtain. A Japanese vegetable with a long history of cultivation in Mibu near Kyoto. Joy Larkcom uses it in winter salads and stir fries, and says that most people like the taste very much.

Green Spray
Closely related to Mizuna greens, and is also a highly decorative plant, forming a dense clump of long narrow, deep green leaves. Has a pleasant mild flavour, and is very versatile in use. Reasonably hardy. (Dob)
SUFF

Millet
Various

Dragon's Claw Millet
Eleusine corocana. An ornamental annual grass with grains held on upright ears, clustered together like fingers. The grains are reddish coloured, and this species is worthy of a trial as a garden crop in warm sunny areas, as it is easily threshed, requires no dehulling and the maturing heads are not particularly attractive to birds. (Futu)
FUTU

Miner's Lettuce
Claytonia perfoliata
Also known as Winter Purslane, and sown in late summer for harvesting for salads through the winter.

Miner's Lettuce
An excellent winter salad crop rich in vitamin C. Available from November to March from August sowing outdoors or in a cold greenhouse. Take a few leaves at a time on a "cut-and-come-again" basis. (OGC)
CGAR; CHAM; CHIL; D&D; EWK; OGC; POYN; SUFF; SUTT

Mitsuba
Cryptotaenia japonica
Also known as Japanese Parley, this, like parsley, is a member of the Umbellifer family. Mitsuba is said to taste of celery, parley and angelica combined.

Mitsuba
Like a cross between parsley and celery with a unique flavour for salads and soups. It can be blanched like celery. (OGC)
CGAR; CGAR; CHIL; D&D; EWK; OGC; POYN; SBS; SMM; SUFF

Mizuna Greens

Brassica rapa var. nipposinica or var. japonica
Related to Komatsuna, these exceptionally pretty plants can be used at any stage, from small seedlings to large plant.

Mizuna

Quick growing with dark green narrow leaves. Ready in 35 days from summer sowing and 60 days from winter sowing under cover. (D&D)
   CGar; Chil; D&D; EWK; Futu; OGC; SbS; SMM; Suff

F1 Tokyo Beau (Kyona)
   T&M

Youzen

Decorative plant with glossy, dark green, deeply serrated leaves. Very versatile, and can be used at any stage from seedlings to maturity to flowering shoots. Mild flavoured, very hardy, and ornamental enough to grow in a flower bed. (Dob)
   Dob

Mustard

Brasicca spp
Grown either as part of the traditional mustard and cress, or as a green manure.

Black
   Cham

Brown
Annual approx 85 days. (Suff)
   Suff

Burgonde
Standard variety for producing French mustard and for hot brown and stoneground mustard. Small brown seed. May also be used as a green manure. (Suff)
   Suff

Fine White
Grow as mustard and cress inside. If grown outside it makes an excellent cut and come again crop. (Suff)
   Mars; SbS; Suff; Unwi; Wall

Mustard
Fine strain and traditional companion to cress. To crop together, sow mustard four days later. (Foth)
   Brwn; Foth; OGC

Tilney
High grade quality shoots for salad use. (EWK)
    CGar; EWK; Rog; Yate

White
The best variety to grow indoors for salads. Should be grown in the same way as cress. (Dob)
    Cart; Cham; Chil; Dob; John; JWB; Sutt

Mustard Greens

Brassica juncea
Another diverse group of oriental brasssicas, also known as Chinese mustard greens and Indian Mustard greens. Gai Choy (Kaai tsoi) is the Cantonese for Mustard Green, and not a variety name, but until the seed suppliers start labelling their varieties properly it will be impossible to place their offerings into the correct group.

Amsoi
Green Indian Mustard. Delicious tender green with a mustard tang for stir fry or salad use. Best sown from June to September for autumn crop. Sow September under cover for spring crop. In most winters should survive outside in seedling stage for early spring cuttings. (Suff)
    Suff

Gai Choy
Many suppliers call this Green in Snow, but strictly Green in Snow is one group of Mustard Greens, and Gai Choy is just another name for Mustard Greens. We need more information if we are to make use of these excellent vegetables.
    CGar; D&D; EWK; Futu; John; OGC; OGC; SbS; SMM; Suff; Sutt; T&M

Kaai Tsoi
Just another spelling of Gai Choy.
    Suff

Red Mustard
The large attractive reddish-green leaves and the stems may be eaten, the leaves being somewhat spicier. Inner leaves have a milder flavour. In addition to use in stir-frying, the leaves may also be steamed or used for pickling. Immature plants may be used in salads. (Dob)
    Dob

Oca

Oxalis tuberosa

Oca

From the Peruvian Andes this attractive yellow flowering herbaceous plant produces a tasty tuber that can be eaten fresh, boiled, stir-fried or used in stews. Grow like a potato. (Poyn)

POYN

Red Skinned

FUTU

White Skinned

FUTU

Okra

Abelmoschus esculentus

Edible pods from a member of the Mallow family. Related to cotton.

F1 Annie Oakley

SUFF

Clemson's Spineless

All America Winner. Probably the most popular variety, producing a heavy crop of high quality dark green lightly grooved spineless pods. Best picked when only 2-3 in. long. (T&M)

CHIL; EWK; FOTH; JOHN; JWB; MOLE; SBS; SMM; T&M; WALL

Dwarf Green Longpod

SBS

Green Velvet

The light green pods are long, slender, straight, smooth and very tender. Vigorous growing and a heavy cropper, with good results easily obtained when raised under glass like tomatoes. (Unwi)

UNWI

Long Green

Grown for its ornamental seed pods, which provide a flavoursome addition to stews, sauces and soups. Sow in February/March and harvest when the pods are young and tender. For greenhouses or sheltered spots outside in warm areas. (Dob)

DOB; SUTT

Okra

BAKK; CGAR

Pent Green
SBS

Onion
Allium cepa
A1
SBS

Agusta Rijnsburger
SBS

Ailsa Craig
An old, tried, tested and favourite variety, suitable for spring or autumn sowing, with large, globe-shaped, mild-flavoured bulbs with rich, straw-coloured skins. (Chil)
BAKK; BRWN; CART; CGAR; CHIL; D&D; DOB; EWK; FOTH; JOHN; JWB; MARS; MAS; MOLE; OGC; ROG; SBS; SMM; SUTT; TUCK; UNWI; VANH; WALL

Ailsa Craig Crosslings Seedling
Giant onion used exclusively for exhibition work. Grows to an immense size weighing several pounds. To obtain best results start in greenhouse, or under glass, in January, plant out as soon as weather permits. Feed regularly and keep well watered. For exhibition onions sow by February 1. (VanH)
ROG; SBS; VANH; WALL

F1 Alamo
BREE; FOTH

F1 Albion
BAKK; MARS; T&M; VANH

Alix
BREE

Autumn Gold
Large, solid onions, half-round in shape. The attractive deep golden skins are really strong and the onions will keep until April or May from a September harvest. The crop is always huge and we have rarely known any bolters. (Mars)
MARS

Autumn Queen see Reliance
Balstora
Balstora produces a very heavy crop of beautiful globe-shaped onions with golden-brown skins. You should expect it to store at least until early May (Mars)
BRWN; DOB; JOHN; MARS; MOLE; SBS; VANH; WALL; YATE

Onion

Barletta
Specially selected for pickling. Sow thickly in the rows in order to obtain beautiful, fine onions. One of the most popular silverskin onions. (Bakk)
> BAKK; MOLE; SBS; SUFF

F1 Beacon
> SMM; T&M

Bedfordshire Champion
Good-sized globe. Long keeper, improved strain. (Mars)
> BRWN; CART; CGAR; CHIL; D&D; DOB; EWK; FOTH; JOHN; JWB; MARS; MAS; MOLE; OGC; ROG; SBS; SMM; SUFF; SUTT; UNWI; WALL

Best Of All
> SBS; TOZE

Brunswick
Flattish round, deep red onion with good keeping qualities. It has an excellent flavour and will give very high yields. (Bakk)
> BAKK; EWK; FOTH; SUTT

Brunswick Red see Brunswick
Brunswijker see Brunswick
F1 Buffalo
> CGAR; DOB; FOTH; JOHN; JWB; MAS; MOLE; SBS; T&M; TOZE; TUCK

F1 Cadix
> BREE

F1 Caribo
> BREE; JOHN; T&M

F1 Centurion
> DOB; EWK; ROG; SUFF; UNWI

Crosslings Seedling see Ailsa Craig Crosslings Seedling
F1 Crusader
> SBS

F1 Dinaro
> RSLU

Dobies' All Rounder
Round straw-coloured onions of fine flavour and of medium size—just right for the kitchen. Being quite thin necked, they keep extremely well in winter storage, remaining in good condition until February and March. Dutch grown. (Dob)
> DOB

Downing Yellow Globe
> SBS

Duraldo
Deep brown skinned, almost round shaped bulbs of fine eating quality and exceptional keeping ability. (EWK)
EWK; SBS

Early Yellow Globe
SBS

Ebeneezer
SBS

F1 Express Harvest Yellow
CGAR; EWK; JWB; MOLE; OGC; ROG; SBS; SUFF; WALL

Express Yellow see Express Harvest Yellow
Extra Early Kaizuka
Flattish bulb ripening to pale yellow. (Sutt)
CGAR; D&D; EWK; JOHN; ROG; SBS; WALL

First Early
Onion sets for autumn sowing which produce a crop in June and July before the spring sown varieties have matured. With medium sized, flat bulbs of mild flavour, this variety is sown in September and will stand all but the most severe of weather conditions. (OGC)
OGC

Giant Fen Globe
Produce a huge crop of perfectly shaped onions, often 50 lb or more from each bag planted. In our trials they give a higher yield than any other onion. They will usually keep until late May and have a fairly mild taste. (Mars)
MARS

Giant Rocca Brown
SBS

Giant Rocca Lemon
SBS

Giant Stuttgarter see Stuttgart Giant
Giant Zittau
Produces excellent medium-sized pickles, pale brown in colour. Sow in March. (Mars)
EWK; MARS; OGC; SBS; TOZE

F1 Gion Festival
YATE

Onion

Golden Ball
A most receptive onion set because it loves to be planted late. At this time the weather is warmer. Hence it avoids some of the pitfalls earlier sets face. It is a very rapid grower and planted 6 weeks later will be ready at approximately the same time as regular varieties and has comparable yield and long storage qualities. (T&M)
> T&M

Golden Bear see Norstar
F1 Goldito
> RSLu

Gros see White Lisbon
Guardsman
A cross between normal spring onion and a Japanese type, it will hold in good condition longer before the stems bulb and become stronger in flavour. You will be able to pull bunches of fine stems with deep green leaves and nice white bases over several weeks from one sowing. (Mars)
> Dob; Mars; Toze

F1 Hamlet
> SbS

Hikari Bunching
A modern type of spring or bunching onion, Hikari is a versatile performer. From a spring sowing, it can be harvested over a long period as it does not form bulbs. Begin pulling at pencil thickness and continue through to the size of a small carrot. Distinctive, delicious taste. (Dob)
> CGar; Dob; JWB; Mole; RSLu; SbS; SMM; Toze; Wall; Yate

F1 Hygro
> Brwn; D&D; Dob; EWK; John; JWB; Mars; Mole; OGC; Rog; SbS; SMM; Toze; Tuck; Unwi; Wall; Yate

F1 Hyper
> SbS

F1 Hyrate
> SbS

F1 Hysam
> Brwn; John; Mole; SbS

F1 Hyton
> John; SbS

Imai see Imai Early Yellow
Imai Early Yellow
Semi-globe shape, maturing from late June. Yellow skin. (Mars)
> JOHN; MARS; MOLE; SBS; YATE

Imai Yellow see Imai Early Yellow
Indared
> YATE

Ishiko Straight Leaf
> YATE

Ishikura
A new bunching onion: a cross between leek and coarse chives. Ishikura is a fast grower. It has beautiful, fairly long, white stems, and dark green leaves. An extremely prolific variety. (Bakk)
> BAKK; CGAR; EWK; FOTH; JOHN; OGC; SBS; SUTT; T&M; TUCK

Ishikura Bunching see Ishikura
Ishikuro see Ishikura
James Long Keeping
A good old variety with a very pleasant taste and first-class looks. The reddish brown, globe-shaped bulbs are excellent keepers. (Foth)
> CGAR; ROG; SBS; WALL

F1 Jet Set
> T&M

Jumbo
It has a golden-brown skin, is a perfect ball shape, large, solid and very uniform. One of the heaviest croppers, with exceptionally good keeping qualities. (Unwi)
> BREE; DOB; SBS

F1 Karato
> BREE

F1 Keepwell
> JOHN; T&M; YATE

Kelsae see The Kelsae
Kyoto Market
> BREE; JOHN; SBS

La Reine see The Queen
Lancastrian
A giant globe shape variety ideal for exhibitions with sweet, crisp, white flesh and golden yellow skin. It is also excellent for cooking and storing. (Foth)
> CGAR; FOTH; JOHN; SMM; T&M

Long Red Florence
The traditional torpedo shaped red onion from Florence in Italy. Very reliable producing good sized bulbs with deep purple red colour. (Suff)
> SUFF

Long White Ishikura see Ishikura
Long White Tokyo
A splendid plant with dark green leaves and the white succulent single stalks grow 16-19ins. long. Fairly resistant to both hot and cold weather, it is good for either a summer or winter crop. (Chil)
> CHIL

F1 Mambo
> BREE

Mammoth
> CGAR; JWB; ROB; WALL

Mammoth Improved see Mammoth
Mammoth Red
Largest red onion in cultivation, has excellent keeping qualities with strong flavour. (CGar)
> CGAR; JWB; ROB; WALL

F1 Maraton
> BAKK; DOB; JOHN

F1 Mardito
> RSLU

F1 Markies
> JOHN

Monkston
Our new introduction which has been bred for exhibition use. Very large bulbs of superb shape and uniformity. (EWK)
> CGAR; EWK; JWB; ROG; SBS; SMM; WALL

Monkston Exhibition see Monkston
Multi-stalk 2
A very fine, early variety with light green leaves and clusters of succulent, long white stalks up to 14ins. in length that are very tender and highly tasty. (Chil)
> CHIL

Multi-stalk 5
This is an excellent bunching onion, and both the leaves and stalks are extremely tender and tasty. Grow in clusters of five or six stalks to about 20-25ins. No waste you can eat it almost all. (Chil)
CHIL

New Brown Pickling
MOLE; SBS

Nocera
SBS

Nordhollandse Bloedrode see North Holland Blood Red
F1 Norstar
BAKK; EWK; OGC; SBS; SUFF

North Holland Blood Red
Large red-skinned globe with crisp, pink flesh throughout. Stores very well. (Foth)
JOHN; T&M; UNWI

North Holland Blood Red Redmate
SUTT

North Holland Flat Yellow
SBS

Oakey see Reliance
Oporto
RSLU; SBS

Paris see Paris Silver Skin
Paris Silver Skin
Excellent "cocktail" pickler. Sow March to late June, lift when about marble size. (Mars)
BRWN; CGAR; EWK; FOTH; JOHN; JWB; MARS; OGC; ROG; SBS; SUTT; TUCK; UNWI; VANH; WALL

F1 Polo
SBS

Pompei
SBS

F1 Puma
DOB

Onion

Purplette
The first ever purple-red skinned mini onion. Decorative and very tasty. The tiny bulbs turn a delicate pink when cooked or pickled. Can also be harvested very young as purple bunching onions. May also be left to harvest at normal size as mature onions. (Suff)
> MOLE; OGC; SBS; SMM; SUFF

Radar
> MOLE; SBS; WALL

Red Baron
Early, prolific, flattish-round to round, deep red onion, suitable for eating fresh as well as for storing. Full-flavoured. Much in demand by the professional as well as by the amateur grower. (Bakk)
> BAKK; DOB; JOHN; JWB; T&M; VANH

Red Brunswick see Brunswick
Red Bunching Redbeard
A completely new bunching onion. Very decorative red stalks with colour extending in 2-4 layers. Extra decorative to use in salads. (Suff)
> OGC; SUFF

Red Delicious
Red Delicious has a shiny deep red skin and crisp white flesh. Good crops of globe-shaped bulbs are produced with good keeping ability. (Dob)
> DOB

Red Italian
> CHIL; SBS

Redmate
> YATE

Reliance
A large, firm, flattish onion, it has a mild flavour and is a wonderful keeper. Recommended for spring sowing but can also be used for autumn sowings. (Unwi)
> JWB; OGC; SBS; SUFF

Rijnsburger
A round onion with yellow skin and pure white flesh. Hard, long-keeping bulbs. (Sutt)
> EWK; JOHN; WALL

Rijnsburger 2 Sito
> FOTH

Rijnsburger 4
> CGAR; ROG; SBS; SMM; SUTT; TOZE

Rijnsburger Rocky
>SBS; SBS; YATE

Rinaldo
>SBS

Robot
A very good onion for storing. Brownish-yellow colour. Extremely high-yielding variety. Robot can deservedly be called one of the best selections. (Bakk)
>BAKK

Robusta
Very heavy cropper with outstanding globe shape, fine quality skin and extremely long keep ability. (EWK)
>CGAR; EWK; JOHN; JWB; MOLE; OGC; SBS

Rocardo
An excellent storing onion. Semi-globes with dark skins and a good flavour and texture. (Foth)
>FOTH; SUTT

F1 Romeo
>JOHN

Rouge d'Italie see Red Italian
F1 Royal Oak
>FOTH; TOZE

SY300
>YATE

Santa Claus
Forms long stalks which do not bulb. Will hold well in the grounds without going tough and from approximately 8 weeks will start to flush red from the base upwards. A good flavour. (Foth)
>FOTH; T&M

Senshyu see Senshyu Semi-Globe
Senshyu Semi-Globe
Like Imai Yellow, but maturing about 2 weeks later. Good sized solid bulbs. (Mars)
>BRWN; CGAR; D&D; EWK; FOTH; JOHN; JWB; MARS; MOLE; OGC; ROG; SBS; SUTT; TOZE; TUCK; UNWI; WALL; YATE

Senshyu Yellow see Senshyu Semi-Globe
F1 Shakespeare
>YATE

Onion

Showmaster
Developed from a top exhibition strain of onion, this special variety will produce the largest onions from onion sets. (Mars)
> Mars

F1 Sonic
> John

Southport Red Globe
A blood-red onion which grows to a large size, very popular with exhibitors and a change for the cook. A good keeper whose ancestors were grown for 17th century sailors. (OGC)
> Brwn; CGar; D&D; EWK; OGC; Rog; SbS; Suff; VanH; Wall

Southport White Globe
> SbS; SbS

Sturon
A considerable improvement of the Stuttgart: extremely prolific globe onion. An excellent variety. Very much recommended! (Bakk)
> Bakk; Bree; CGar; D&D; EWK; John; Rog; Tuck; Unwi

Stuttgart Giant
Flattish round onion which will keep for a fairly long time. However, the most important feature is that this variety can be harvested early. (Bakk)
> Bakk; CGar; D&D; EWK; John; Mars; OGC; Rog; Tuck; Unwi

Stuttgarter Riesen see Stuttgart Giant
F1 Super Bear
> EWK

F1 Sweet Sandwich
> T&M

Tamrock
> Yate

F1 Targa
> SbS

Tarzan
> SbS

The Kelsae
> CGar; JWB; Wall

The Queen
True silver skin. Sow thickly and the resultant competition will prevent the bulbs from getting too large for pickling purposes. (Dob)
> Cart; Dob

The Sutton Globe see Bedfordshire Champion

Toro
> TOZE

F1 Toronto
> BREE

Torpedo
Combining the flavour of a shallot with the sweetness of a Spanish onion is this most attractive-looking variety with smallish, red, torpedo-shaped bulbs. Thinly sliced, they add both savour and eye appeal to any salad. They can be sown in spring for a summer harvest or late summer for use the following year. (Chil)
> CHIL

F1 Tough Ball
> YATE

Turbo
Exceptional onions which are vigorous, have high bolt resistance and store well. Very popular. (Foth)
> BREE; CGAR; D&D; EWK; FOTH; OGC; ROG; T&M; TUCK

Unwin's Exhibition
Under average garden conditions, it will easily produce huge, top quality onions of about a pound in weight and, with a little bit of tender loving care, you will be able to go way beyond this figure. (Unwi)
> UNWI

White Knight
There are usually few salad onions in June, because the overwintered crop has ended and spring sowings are not ready. It is possible to raise a fine crop of White Knight in this period by sowing in Propapacks in early February, transplanting outdoors in early April. Can also be sown outdoors from March onwards. (Mars)
> MARS

White Lisbon
A very popular salad onion with a particularly fine flavour for using fresh in various dishes and in salads. Pull the small white onions and cut off the top ends, leaving approx 20-25 cm. of the hollow leaves. (Bakk)
> BAKK; BREE; BRWN; CART; CGAR; CHIL; D&D; DOB; EWK; FOTH; JOHN; JWB; MARS; MOLE; OGC; ROG; RSLU; SBS; SMM; SUFF; SUTT; T&M; TOZE; TUCK; UNWI; VANH; WALL; YATE

White Lisbon Winter Hardy see Winter-over

F1 White Spear
Grows to a good size and has a very mild flavour. (JWB)
> FOTH; JOHN; SBS; YATE

White Sweet Spanish
Grows to a good size and has a very mild flavour. (JWB)
> JWB; SbS

Wigbo
> SbS

Winter Standing see Winter-over
Winter White Bunching
Stiffer, stronger foliage than White Lisbon. Can be pulled in May from an August or September sowing. Slower to bulb than other over-wintering salad onions. (Mars)
> MARS; T&M; TOZE

Winter-over
Stands severe weather. Only suitable for autumn sowing. (Brwn)
> BREE; CGAR; D&D; DOB; EWK; FOTH; JOHN; MOLE; OGC; ROG; RSLU; SBS; SMM; SUTT; UNWI; WALL; YATE

Yellow Globe Danvers
> SbS

F1 Yellowstone (Topkeeper)
> JOHN

Zittauer Gelbe see Giant Zittau
Zur Robal
> BREE

Onion Other
Allium spp

Babington Leek
An uncommon native of coastal localities, this relative of the leek produces garlic-like cloves that can be eaten, as well as young stems that can be treated like leeks. The flowerheads produce numerous bulbils that can be sown to produce more plants. (Futu)
> FUTU

Potato Onion
An onion that grows from offsets like shallots. Each bulb divides underground to form a clump of 6-8 mild flavoured onions that can be stored for several months. It is said to be very pest and disease resistant. (Futu)
> FUTU

Red Welsh Onion
Use the green leaves like chives for flavouring, especially in the Winter. Has a milder flavour than the tree onion. (Poyn)
POYN; SUFF

Tree Onion
An intriguing herb which bears clusters of small onions on the tips of its stems; delicious in salads or as pickles. The foliage may be cut throughout Winter. (Poyn)
FUTU; POYN; SMM

Welsh Onion
Perennial type, forming thickened and fleshy leaf bases instead of bulb. Useful for pulling as Spring Onions. Sow February-May where the plants are to grow. (Dob)
CGAR; D&D; EWK; FOTH; FUTU; MARS; POYN; SBS; SMM; UNWI; VANH

Orache
Atriplex hortensis
Also known as Mountain Spinach, and long grown for its succulent leaves.

Green
CHAM; FUTU

Red
CHAM; FUTU; SBS

Pak Choi
Brassica rapa var. chinensis
Joy Larkcom is strict about reserving the name Pak Choi for this particular vegetable, and not confusing it with Headed Chinese Cabbage. There are many different types, each with different characteristics and uses, and in China the leaves are often dried in the sun for use in soups during winter.

F1 Joi Choi
A sturdy plant with wide, short leaf stalks that are white and flat. Very productive.
BREE; JOHN; MARS; OGC; SMM; SUFF; UNWI; YATE

F1 Kaneko Cross
DOB

F1 Mei Quing
The name means "beautiful green," referring to the green leaf stalks.
T&M

Parsley

Pak Choi
A novel Chinese vegetable of increasing popularity. Very versatile. The young central leaves may be used fresh in salads, the mature leaves have a mild flavour when cooked and the white leaf stalks are succulently tender. Tasty when boiled, steamed or stir-fried. Slow to bolt, should be sown in March-April and again in late summer. (Dob)
> CHIL; DOB; EWK; JWB; SBS; SMM; SUTT

Tai-Sai
A soup-spoon variety, with elegant curved leaf stalks.
> BAKK; CGAR

White Celery Mustard
A soup-spoon type, with thinner leaf stalks.
> CHIL; OGC; SBS; SMM

Par-Cel

Par-Cel
Looks like parsley, tastes like celery. Instead of a parsley garnish that is left on the side of the plate, Par-cel is the garnish with the real celery flavour that you can eat too. Fast becoming a basic salad ingredient it's plentiful, can be grown as easily as radishes and gives a salad that wonderful warm celery flavour. (T&M)
> T&M

Parsley
Petroselinum crispum
Berliner and Hamburg are grown for their roots, the others for their leaves.

Berliner
A tasty, fleshy vegetable. The highly aromatic, beautiful, smooth roots are very tender when cooked. Extraordinarily fine flavour. Roots can be stored. (Bakk)
> BAKK; UNWI

Bravour
Really dark green finely curled leaves. Very hardy and stands for a long time. (EWK)
> BAKK; BRWN; CGAR; EWK; JOHN; MOLE; ROG; SBS; TOZE; TUCK; UNWI; WALL; YATE

Calito
A vigorous and heavy yielding selection maintaining its colour well when overwintered in mild areas. Slightly looser curled than Bravour. (Yate)
> YATE

Champion
DOB

Champion Moss Curled
A highly selected strain, with curled intense green leaves. Stands much better than other varieties. (OGC)
JOHN; MOLE; OGC; SBS; TOZE; TUCK; VANH

Clivi
Dwarf, very neat and prolific. The only variety whose base leaves do not turn yellow and have to be wasted. (T&M)
SBS; T&M; YATE

Common
Has a stronger and more pungent flavour than the curled variety. Produces dark green sturdy plants with a great deal of bulk. Much used on the Continent. (OGC)
BAKK; EWK; MARS; MOLE; OGC; ROG; SUTT; T&M; WALL

Consort
SBS

Curled
Very sturdy in growth with good length stems and densely curled heads. (EWK)
EWK; POYN; ROG

Curlina
A very compact, short-stemmed variety with tightly curled leaves. (Mars)
CART; DOB; FOTH; MARS; SBS; UNWI

Darki
Really compact, dark green heads on long stems for easy cutting. Heavy yielding variety. (EWK)
EWK; JOHN; SBS; YATE

Envy
Dark green densely curled foliage. (Dob)
DOB; SUTT

French
Biennial, 18 in., rich soil. Stronger flavour than curled. (D&D)
CGAR; D&D; POYN; SBS

Frisco
Similar to Afro but with heavier stems, tighter curl and somewhat more vigour. Suitable for all sowing periods. (Bree)
BREE

Parsley

Gigante di Napoli see Italian Giant Leaved
Halblange see Berliner
Hamburg Omega Turnip Rooted
An excellent dual purpose variety whose leaves can be used as ordinary parsley for garnishing or in soups or stew. White parsnip-shaped roots have a distinctive flavour and are delicious when roasted. For sowing from March-May. Winter hardy. (Dob)
> DOB; T&M

Hamburg Turnip Rooted
Grown mainly for its parsnip-like roots which, when lifted in the autumn, can be sliced or grated for added flavour on salads. (EWK)
> CGAR; EWK; FOTH; FUTU; JOHN; JWB; MARS; OGC; ROG; SBS; SMM; SUFF; SUTT; VANH; WALL

Italian Giant
Biennial, 2ft 6in in rich soil, vigorous. Strongest flavour. (D&D)
> POYN

Italian Plain Leaf
> D&D; YATE

Korte see Hamburg Turnip Rooted
Mooskrause see Champion Moss Curled
Moss Curled
Very compact and has very finely curled leaves. Excellent for cutting, gives a distinctive flavour to soups, sauces and fish dishes. (Bakk)
> BAKK; CGAR; FOTH; JWB; TOZE; WALL

Moss Curled 2
Popular sort, dark green. Long standing. (Mars)
> CART; DOB; MARS; SUTT

Moss Curled 2 Green Velvet
Beautiful, fully curled, piquantly flavoured variety with rich deep green appearance. (T&M)
> T&M

Moss Curled Afro
Distinct from ordinary Moss-Curled in having heavier stems, with much tighter curl and strikingly darker colour. Very heavy yielding, and is suitable for autumn and spring sowings. (Bree)
> BREE; T&M

Moss Curled Extra Triple Curled
> SBS; SMM

Moss Curled Krausa
Widely used in Holland by the majority of housewifes. Moss Curled very uniform rich green leaves. Flavours many dishes in addition to its garnishing value. Outstanding Dutch herb. (VanH)
JOHN; VANH

New Dark Green
SBS

Peerless
SBS

Plain see Common
Plain Leaved see Common
Regent
SBS

Robust
TOZE

Sheeps see Common
Thujade
Strong, curled, extremely dark green variety which, because of its dark colour, is preferred for use as a garnish. (Bakk)
BAKK

Triplex
RSLU

Verbo
Dark green colour with long stem. Highly productive with good standing. (Brwn)
BRWN; JOHN

Verdi
SBS

Parsnip
Pastinacea sativa
Alba
A refined prepacking variety of the same general shape as Cobham Improved Marrow but more slender, whiter and still less susceptible to canker. (Toze)
JOHN; SBS; TOZE

Avonresister
Small conical roots, resistant to canker. (Mars)
BRWN; CART; CGAR; D&D; EWK; FOTH; JOHN; MARS; MAS; MOLE; OGC; ROG; SBS; T&M; TUCK; UNWI; VANH; WALL; YATE

Parsnip

Bayonet
Slender, length to 10 in. and modest 2.5 in. diameter shoulders. Very canker resistant. (Foth)
> FOTH; SBS; UNWI

Bedford Monarch
> SBS

Cambridge Improved Marrow
> SBS

Cobham Improved Marrow
Selected for quality and resistance to canker, a very good medium-sized parsnip of tapering shape. The white roots are smooth-skinned and of fine flavour. (Dob)
> CART; DOB; MARS; TOZE

Dobies Intermediate
Suitable for soils that are not deep enough to grow the long-rooted varieties. Small leaved, flavoursome roots. (Dob)
> DOB

Evesham
> SBS

Exhibition Long
Extra long variety for the exhibitor, flavour and cooking quality is excellent. (Rob)
> CGAR; DOB; JWB; ROB; WALL

Gigantic
This hybrid variety has been bred for exceptional size and vigour to such an extent it has yielded one of the world's longest and one of the heaviest parsnips ever. (T&M)
> T&M

F1 Gladiator
> BREE; BRWN; FOTH; JOHN; OGC; SUTT; T&M; TOZE

Harris Model
> SBS

Hollow Crown
Large wide shouldered type with long tapering roots. (EWK)
> BAKK; BRWN; CART; CGAR; CHIL; D&D; EWK; FOTH; JOHN; JWB; MOLE; OGC; ROG; SBS; TUCK; VANH; WALL

Hollow Crown Improved
An improved stock of this long-rooted type. (Dob)
> DOB; UNWI

Parsnip

Imperial Crown
Long, high quality roots of excellent flavour. Much smaller crown than usual in this type. (EWK)
 EWK; Rog; SbS; Wall

Improved Marrow
 SbS; Yate

F1 Javelin
 Foth; Toze

Lancer
Mini-vegetable. A new Bayonet-type Parsnip, similar to those frequently seen in the larger supermarkets. Very smooth-skinned and its uniformly coloured flesh is superbly tasty. Very resistant to canker. (Dob)
 Dob; T&M; Toze

Lisbonnais
 Foth; John; JWB; Mole; SbS

New White Skin
A British bred variety with uniform wedge-shaped roots and a pure white skin which does not discolour after washing. Good canker resistance. (Sutt)
 Sutt

Offenham
Half-long type with cream coloured flesh. Excellent quality and heavy cropper. (EWK)
 EWK; JWB; Rog; SbS; VanH; Wall

Tender and True
Ideal for exhibition or kitchen. Long and smooth, very little core. (Mars)
 CGar; D&D; Dob; EWK; Foth; John; Mars; MAS; OGC; Rog; SbS; SMM; Suff; Sutt; T&M; Tuck; Wall

The Student
Long slender roots of good size and flavour. (EWK)
 CGar; D&D; EWK; OGC; Rog; SbS; SMM; Wall

Viceroy
 SbS

White Diamond
 SbS

Pea

White Gem
Broad-shouldered smooth roots of good size with a fine white skin and considerable canker-tolerance. Excellent flavour. Very early and easy to lift. Superior to Offenham. (Mars)
> BRWN; CGAR; JOHN; JWB; MARS; RSLU; SBS; SUFF; SUTT; TUCK; UNWI; YATE

White King
Very white flesh. Long tapering root. (D&D)
> D&D; EWK; OGC; ROG; SBS; VANH; WALL

White Spear
An improvement in the White Gem type with greater uniformity. (Bree)
> BREE; JOHN; TOZE

Yatesnip
> YATE

Pea

Pisum sativum

Round peas are generally hardier than wrinkled peas, but not as tasty. Sugar peas are eaten pod and all.

American Wonder
A sweet, early pea. This much-prized variety can be grown without wire netting or twiggy sticks on humus-rich soils. It produces a heavy crop of long pods with very tasty peas. Ht 45 cm. (Bakk)
> BAKK

Granada
> RSLU

Lambado
> BREE

Markado
> BREE

Masterfon
Marrowfat variety used for the production of dried peas. Ht 2 ft. (JWB)
> RSLU

Minado
> BREE

Minnow
The first UK bred, true Petit Pois Pea. Produces massive crops of narrow stump pods containing approximately 8 small, mid-green tasty peas. Ht 2 ft. (Dob)
> DOB

Nomad
BREE

Nordic
BREE

Petit Pois
True French type with masses of tiny, very sweet tasting peas. (EWK)
D&D; EWK

Revolution
BREE

Skinado
BREE

Sparkle
BREE

Thomas Laxton
Early main crop, a good cropper with blunt-ended pods and sweet flavoured peas.
Ht 3 ft. (OGC)
SBS

Pea Round

Bountiful
A prolific, very early variety, highly valued by many, also by professional growers.
This variety produces well-filled pods. Ht 140 cm. (Bakk)
BAKK

Doublette
A very early, if not the earliest variety. Fine pea for preserving. Excellent quality
and flavour. Dark green colour. Extraordinarily prolific. Ht 60 cm. (Bakk)
BAKK

Douce Provence
Sweeter than Feltham First and just as hardy. Ht 2 ft. (Mars)
FOTH; JOHN; JWB; MARS; MOLE; ROG

Edelkrombek
Very popular, smooth-seeded variety (yellow-seeded). It produces tall plants, approx
140-160 cm. in height, carrying lots of long pods, packed with delicious, juicy peas.
(Bakk)
BAKK

Feltham Advance
ROG; SBS

Pea Sugar

Feltham First
An early, hardy variety with large, slightly curved painted pods. Ht 45 cm. (Bree)
BREE; BRWN; CART; CGAR; D&D; DOB; EWK; FOTH; JOHN; JWB; MARS; MAS; MOLE; OGC; ROG; SBS; SHAR; SMM; SUTT; TOZE; TUCK; UNWI; VANH; WALL; YATE

Fortune
An early variety, slightly later than Feltham but a heavy cropper. 45 cm. (Brwn)
BRWN; JOHN; ROG; SBS

Galaxie
BREE

Gladiator see Fillbasket
Meteor
Very dwarf habit, ht 14 in. (35 cm). Small well filled pods. First early. (EWK)
BAKK; D&D; EWK; FOTH; JOHN; JWB; MOLE; OGC; ROG; SBS; SHAR; SUFF; UNWI; WALL

Petit Provencal see Meteor
Pilot
Very hardy variety for early spring or autumn sowing. Ht 36 in. (90 cm.). Long podded. First early. (EWK)
D&D; EWK; JOHN; JWB; OGC; ROG; SBS

Prince Albert
An early, vigorously growing variety. This selection can be sown early. It will produce a bumper crop of yellowish-green peas. Ht 1 m. (Bakk)
BAKK

Superb
JWB; SBS

Pea Sugar

De Grace see Sugar Dwarf De Grace
Delikett
RSLU

Edula
It can be grown unsupported but we would advise short sticks or netting. The curved pods may be cooked whole when young; later the sweet, green peas can be shelled out. Height 90cms. (Unwi)
UNWI

Heraut
An early, heavy-cropping variety, very much in demand. It produces tender sugar peas, full of flavour. Should be trained upwards. Ht 140 cm. (Bakk)
BAKK

Honey Pod
The earliest snap pea and indeed the sweetest. Producing smaller pods but many more of them than any other snap pea on a compact plant. They are also easier to harvest breaking cleanly without pulling the plant to pieces. (T&M)
BREE; T&M

Mange Tout
Eat all. (CGar)
CGAR; VANH

Nofila
An outstanding early Sugar Pea with broad fleshy pods. Nofila has been bred to produce heavy crops on dwarf growing plants, ideally suited to the lack of space in modern gardens. Harvest the young pods whole and serve raw in salads or lightly cooked in other dishes. Ht 15 in. (Dob)
DOB

Norli see Sugar Dwarf Sweet Green

Oregon Sugar Pod
Among the best of mange-tout with a particularly good flavour. Harvest while the pods are still flat and peas only just forming. (Foth)
BREE; CART; EWK; FOTH; JOHN; JWB; MARS; MAS; SHAR; SUTT; T&M; TOZE; UNWI; YATE

Reuzensuiker
Extra large, wide and fleshy pods, about 4 in. long, produced on compact plants which need little support. Begin harvesting the pods as soon as they are large enough to pull and finish when the seeds inside start to swell. Very sweet. Ht 3 ft. (Mars)
JOHN; ROG

Snowflake
More compact and later maturing variety than Oregon Sugar Pod with a similar medium long flat pod. (Bree)
BREE

Sugar Ann
Very productive with big, fully edible pods on dwarf vines with juicy sweet flesh. Use fresh or cooked with or without the pods. (T&M)
FOTH; JOHN; ROG; T&M; TOZE; TUCK

Pea Sugar

Sugar Bon
An early maturing variety with medium length straw and medium-large pale green pods. Very easy to harvest. (Bree)
> Bree; Mars; Rog; Sutt

Sugar Dwarf De Grace
> Mole; Rog; RSlu

Sugar Dwarf Sweet Green
Yields a fine crop of sweetly flavoured pods. White flowers. Ht 3 ft. (Dob)
> Bakk; Bree; Brwn; Chil; D&D; Dob; EWK; Foth; John; Mole; OGC; Rog; SbS; Shar; Suff; T&M; Toze; Tuck; Unwi; Wall

Sugar Gem
Excellent quality, medium sized, sweet, crisp and succulent pods. Lightly cook, stir-fry or eat raw in salads or in the garden. They need good growing conditions and are not suited to wetter areas or seasons but otherwise, unlike other varieties, because of its mildew resistance, can be sown in succession through the summer to crop through the autumn. The first completely stringless and powdery mildew tolerant snap pea. (T&M)
> T&M

Sugar Lil
A main season variety with almost stringless large dark green pods on a vigorous plant. (Bree)
> Bree

Sugar Luv
> Bree

Sugar Rae
A late type to follow Sugar Lil with similar large dark green pods. (Bree)
> Brwn; Cart; Dob; EWK; OGC; Rog

Sugar Snap
Very long season of use. The pods are thick and fleshy and can be eaten as well as the peas—served together or separately. When young, the pods are stringless. More mature pods can have the strings removed very easily. Very sweet. Ht 5 ft. (Mars)
> CGar; Chil; D&D; EWK; Foth; John; JWB; Mars; OGC; Rog; SbS; SMM; Suff; Sutt; T&M; Tuck; VanH

Sugar Tall White
> Shar

Zuga
Mange tout, cooked whole when young. Ht 5 ft. (JWB)
> John; Rog

Pea Wrinkled

Alderman
Tall growing variety which needs support. Very heavy crops of long, well filled pods. Late maincrop. (EWK)
CGar; D&D; Dob; EWK; Foth; John; JWB; Mars; OGC; Rog; SbS; Shar; Suff; Unwi; VanH; Wall

Almota
RSlu

Avola
A vigorous grower in almost all kinds of weather. The peas have a dark green colour. They have an excellent flavour and lend themselves particularly well to deep-freezing. Ht 70 cm. (Bakk)
Bakk; Toze

Banff
A very vigorous early variety suitable for picking fresh and freezing. Three inch-long pods contain medium sized-peas of excellent flavour. Ht 2 ft. (OGC)
OGC; Rog

Bikini
The most widely grown semi-leafless type, with high yield and excellent processing quality, unique variety, semi-fasciated and highly concentrated pod set for maximum yield at freezing stage. (Bree)
Bree; John; Rog

Cavalier
A heavy cropping variety, producing masses of pods, mostly in pairs, each containing 10-11 sweet, small peas. Very good resistance to mildew making it ideal for June-July sowings, in addition to main season. Ht 60-75 cm. (2-2.5 ft). (Sutt)
Brwn; Mars; Sutt; Toze

Chancelot see Lord Chancellor
Coral
A high yielding early pea with a strongly determinate growth habit. Ht 60 cm. (Bree)
Bree

Daisy
A short (2 ft) main crop producing a heavy yield of excellent quality peas, 8-10 peas per pod. (OGC)
SbS

Pea Wrinkled

Darfon
Petit-pois. A new mid-late season variety producing a heavy pick of well filled pods giving an excellent yield of small dark-green peas. Its open habit helps to make picking easier. Ht 2-2.5 ft. (John)
JOHN; ROG

Daybreak
Exceptionally large, blunt pods hold approx. 8 sweet peas. A heavy yielder which can achieve a heigh of 2ft. A good recent introduction. (Foth)
BAKK; BREE; FOTH; T&M

Early Onward
Heavy cropper, large blunt pods, ready 8-10 days ahead of Onward. Ht 60 cm. (Bree)
BREE; BRWN; CGAR; CHIL; D&D; DOB; EWK; JOHN; JWB; MARS; MAS; MOLE; OGC; ROG; RSLU; SBS; SHAR; SUTT; TOZE; TUCK; UNWI; WALL; YATE

Ezetha's Krombek Blauwschok
The pods are bluish-violet in colour. The colour of the flowers is red. Ezetha can be sown for immediate use (at a young stage) as well as for drying (in which case they can be stored for used in the winter. Ht 180 cm. (Bakk)
BAKK

Gradus
(1890) A second early variety ready in late June from and early April sowing. Good sweet flavour. (OGC)
CGAR; EWK; JOHN; JWB; OGC; ROG; SBS; TUCK; WALL

Holiday
ROG; SUTT

Hurst Beagle
Several days earlier than Kelvedon Wonder, this variety is truly sweet tasting. Blunt well-filled pods. Ht. 1.5 ft. (Mars)
EWK; FOTH; JOHN; JWB; MARS; MOLE; ROG; SBS; SHAR; TOZE; TUCK; UNWI; VANH

Hurst Green Shaft
Carries a heavy crop of 4-4.5 in. pods of exhibition standard, which mature over a longer period than most varieties. Beautifully sweet peas. Ht 2.5 ft. (Mars)
BRWN; CART; CGAR; CHIL; D&D; DOB; EWK; FOTH; JOHN; JWB; MARS; MOLE; OGC; ROG; SBS; SHAR; SMM; SUFF; SUTT; T&M; TOZE; TUCK; UNWI; VANH; WALL

Jof
Tall late variety with plenty of vigour. Concentrated pod set at top of fine leaved plant. Ht 90 cm. (Bree)
  BREE

Johnson's Freezer
This wrinkled seeded, maincrop variety is in great demand with food processors, being an excellent freezing variety. It is an abundant cropper, giving peas of excellent quality and flavour, the pods being borne in pairs on dark green vines. Ht 2ft. Not suitable for autumn sowing. (John)
  JOHN; ROG

Kelvedon Monarch see Victory Freezer
Kelvedon Triumph
  ROG; SBS

Kelvedon Wonder
An early variety with narrow tapering pointed pods. Suitable for freezing. Ht 45 cm. (Bree)
  BAKK; BRWN; CART; CGAR; CHIL; D&D; DOB; EWK; FOTH; JOHN; JWB; MARS; MOLE; OGC; ROG; SBS; SHAR; SMM; SUFF; SUTT; T&M; TOZE; TUCK; UNWI; VANH; WALL

Kodiak
This mid season large podded pea has a high resistance to disease and is ideal for organic growing. 65 cm. (Brwn)
  BRWN; ROG

Laxton's Progress No. 9 see Progress No. 9
Lincoln
Very sweet flavoured peas. Heavy cropper, with dark green, curved pods. Ht 24 in. (60 cm). Maincrop. (EWK)
  CGAR; D&D; EWK; JOHN; JWB; OGC; ROG; SBS; SHAR; TUCK

Little Marvel
A proven sort, one of the most popular varieties. Ht 1.5 ft. (Mars)
  CGAR; D&D; DOB; EWK; FOTH; JOHN; JWB; MARS; OGC; ROG; SBS; SHAR; SUTT; T&M; UNWI; VANH; WALL

Lord Chancellor
A later maturing pea. Very heavy crop of dark green pointed pods. Very reliable. Ht 90-120 cm. (3-4 ft). (Sutt)
  ROG; SBS; SUTT

Pea Wrinkled

Lynx
Petit pois type. A really sweet tasting and tender variety becoming increasingly popular for the home gardener looking for something different. 95 cm. (Brwn)
BRWN; JOHN

Markana
When grown in rows 6-12 in. apart the extra tendrils of this sort help the strong-growing plant to support themselves without sticks and the seedlings are not attacked so frequently by birds. The numerous 3. 5-4 in. pods are held in pairs, each containing 8-9 medium-sized, deep green peas with a good flavour. Ht 2 ft. (Mars)
D&D; DOB; EWK; JOHN; MARS; OGC; ROG; TUCK; WALL; YATE

Miracle
Good quality peas on medium tall plants 4. 5 ft (135 cm.). Useful freezing variety. Second early. (EWK)
EWK; JWB; ROG; SBS

Multistar
Uniform in growth with dark green sweet tasting peas. For best results this variety should be sown thinly. Excellent for freezing. Maincrop. (EWK)
CGAR; EWK; VANH; WALL

Onward
The main pea. Easy to pick. Ht 2. 5 ft. (Mars)
BREE; BRWN; CART; CGAR; CHIL; D&D; DOB; EWK; FOTH; JOHN; JWB; MARS; MAS; MOLE; OGC; ROG; RSLU; SBS; SHAR; SMM; SUTT; T&M; TOZE; TUCK; UNWI; VANH; WALL; YATE

Orcado
Main season variety with concentrated pod set at top of plant reducing harvest time and costs. Fine leaved. Ht 75 cm. (Bree)
BREE

Progress No. 9
Long podded variety with heavy yields of dark green, pointed pods. Ht 18 in. (45 cm.). Early. (EWK)
DOB; EWK; JOHN; JWB; MOLE; ROG; SBS; SHAR

Puget
Three, four even five podded pea. Harvesting is easy, just gather in bunches. It's broken all cropping records on trials and, unlike other multi-podded varieties, the peas are of good size. Supreme for freezing, very sweet with an extra high sugar content and retained over a long cropping period. Invaluable if you are able to harvest them immediately. (T&M)
T&M

Recette
SʙS

Senator
An exceptionally heavy cropper, ideal for the amateur gardener. The best main
season variety. (Foth)
Baĸĸ; Foth; Sutt

Show Perfection
Reliably produces an abundance of narrow pods about 6 in. long and packed with
round, dark green peas. Excellent flavour. (Dob)
Brwn; CGar; Dob; JWB; Rob; Sutt

Telephone Nain see Daisy
Top Pod
An excellent all rounder and a great improvement on Onward, it produces more
pods containing nine to ten peas compared with Onward's six to seven. Resistant
to fusarium and powdery mildew, which is a breakthrough for varieties of this type.
(T&M)
T&M

Twiggy
An afila or leafless type, with large, easy to pick pods at the top of the plant. The
leafless habit with intertwining tendrils means the plant stands up much better to
the weather, making picking easier. Powdery mildew resistant. Ht 100 cm. (Bree)
Bree; Foth; T&M

Uniroy
RSʟᴜ

Victory Freezer
SʙS

Walton
Mole

Waverex
Produces a very heavy crop of blunt pods containing small, very sweet peas, some-
times called Petit Pois. Excellent for freezing. Ht 2.5 ft. (Mars)
CGar; Chil; Foth; John; JWB; Mars; OGC; Rog; SMM; Suff; Sutt; Tuck

Pepino
Solanum muricatum
A frost-tender, low-growing shrub that needs similar conditions to the tomato. The pepino
bears large fruits with a flavour similar to that of a melon, with a hint of pear. Cross
pollination improves yields, so grow more than one plant. Cuttings strike very easily, so

small plants can be overwintered indoors for planting out the following season.

Pepino
YATE
FUTU

Pepper Hot
Capsicum annuum
Hot and sweet peppers are botanically identical.

F1 Antler
YATE

F1 Apache
BRWN; DOB; JOHN; MOLE; SUTT

Cayenne
Most useful in pickles, curries, sauces and on pizza. (Foth)
FOTH; JWB; MOLE; SBS; UNWI

Cayenne Long Slim
The best-known hot Cayenne pepper, much used for flavouring exotic meat dishes and sauces. The flavour of these peppers tends to get hotter when they are kept for a longer period of time. (Bakk)
BAKK; JOHN

Chili
Beware, they are very hot! For greenhouse production or indoors, this variety produces a mass of small pods, cropping over a long period. (OGC)
CGAR; D&D; EWK; OGC; ROG; SUTT; WALL

Crespin
An early and very high yielding semi-hot pepper. The conical fruits grow to 3-4 in. in length and increase in heat and flavour as they go from green to red. A medium-tall plant. (Suff)
SUFF

Ethiopian
This is an excellent variety of chilli pepper. Early prolific and firey hot. The long thin pods get hotter as they mature, and turn from green to red. A compact bushy plant. (Suff)
SUFF

F1 Hero
T&M

Hot Mexican
Bushy, compact plants carrying a profusion of 1-1.5 in. long chillis which turn red when ripe. (Mars)
MARS

Hungarian Wax
Vigorous habit with long pointed yellow fruit. Not quite as hot as chillis but warm enough! (OGC)
OGC; SBS; SUFF

F1 Jalapa
YATE

Jalapeno
"Pizza" peppers are most unusual and not for the faint-hearted. Hot! Pendant shaped, blunt ends and thick walls. The fruit size is 2.5 in. and is a medium green to red on maturity. (Foth)
FOTH; SBS; SUFF

Karlo
Yellow wax type Romanian cone shaped pepper up to 3 in. wide x 3-4 in. long. Colour changes to orange and then red when mature. Impressive crop on short and compact plant. Flavour is mildly pungent for eating raw in salad or for cooking. (Suff)
SUFF

No Name
CHIL

Red Cherry
A novel, attractive variety bearing a heavy crop of large cherry sized, green fruits which ripen to red on maturity. Ideal for use in curries, pickles and sauces. (Sutt)
SUTT

Serrano Chili
Greenhouse or indoors only. Only 1.5 in. long, smothered in fruit and the hottest little devils you'll ever taste. A popular Mexican variety eaten fresh, either green or red or can be dried. (T&M)
SUFF; T&M

F1 Super Cayenne
T&M

Tabasco Habanero
A small fruited, very hot variety. Will really knock your socks off. (T&M)
T&M

Pepper Sweet

F1 Ace
Mars; Unwi

F1 Actio
EWK

F1 Antaro
D&D; Tuck; VanH

F1 Ariane
Bakk; CGar; EWK; Foth; John; Mole; OGC; SbS; VanH

F1 Atol
Bakk

F1 Bell Boy
Bree; Brwn; CGar; D&D; Dob; EWK; John; JWB; Mole; OGC; Rog; RSlu; SbS; SMM; Toze; Tuck; Wall; Yate

F1 Bendigo
John; Mole; Toze; Wall

F1 Bianca
Mole

F1 Big Bertha
T&M

F1 Blondy
Bree

Bull Nose Red
SbS

California Wonder
Very pleasant mild flavour. (Mars)
Chil; Foth; John; Mars; Mole; SbS; Unwi; Wall

F1 Canape
Cart; Dob; SMM; T&M; Unwi

F1 Carnival Mixed
Mars

F1 Clio
Mars

F1 Delphin
Brwn; Mole; Yate

F1 Eagle
Brwn

F1 Early Prolific
MARS

Golden Bell
Impressive pepper with open habit and good fruit setting. The blocky fruits start green maturing to bright yellow giving extra colour to salads. (T&M)
T&M

Golden Calwonder
SBS

F1 Gypsy
FOTH; SUTT; T&M

Jingle Bells
The earliest maturing pepper we know. Ideal for containers or where space is limited and a super cropper. Loads of miniature sweet bell peppers which turn red at maturity. Delicious in salads, stir-fries or stuffed. (T&M)
T&M

F1 Jumbo
T&M

F1 Kendo
JOHN

F1 Kerala
RSLU

F1 Leila
BREE

Long Red Marconi
Long thin, deep red pods of mild sweet flavour. Very productive. (EWK)
EWK; WALL

F1 Luteus
BAKK; BRWN; EWK; MOLE; SUTT

Marconi
Large red fruits. Good cropper. (D&D)
CGAR; D&D; ROG; SBS; SUFF

F1 Mavras
BAKK; EWK; MOLE; SBS; WALL

F1 Midnight Beauty
SUTT

F1 New Ace
FOTH; JOHN; MOLE; OGC; SBS; SUFF

Pepper Sweet

F1 Panda
BREE

F1 Propa Rumba
MOLE; WALL

F1 Queen Star
T&M

F1 Rainbow Mixed
FOTH

F1 Redskin
BRWN; CGAR; DOB; EWK; FOTH; JOHN; MOLE; OGC; SUTT; T&M; UNWI

F1 Ringo
SUFF

F1 Rubens
SUFF

Salad Festival
The bright mixture of fruit colours will add interest to your salads. Immature fruits of green, deep purple or cream turn red or gold as they ripen. All are of best greenhouse quality. (Unwi)
UNWI

F1 Sirono
RSLU

F1 Slim Pim
OGC; SBS; SUFF

Sunnybrook
Sixty cm. tall plants. When they are red and ripe they can be used either raw or cooked in a great diversity of dishes such as salads and casseroles or stew. (Bakk)
BAKK

F1 Super Set
BAKK

Sweet Green
SBS

Sweet Spanish Mixed
Yellow, red (and green) sweet peppers. Good cropper. (D&D)
CGAR; D&D; ROG; SBS; VANH

F1 Tequila
BRWN

Worldbeater
Fruits in abundance. Best grown under glass, but can be transplanted outdoors in June in warm, sheltered areas. (Sutt)
SUTT

Yellow Lantern
Reliably produces heavy crops of block-shaped, 4-lobed fruits which are first green, turning to golden-yellow when ripe. (Dob)
DOB

Yolo Wonder
An open pollinated type, which has large square fruits and is pleasantly mild. (OGC)
OGC

Pepper-Tomato hybrid
Top Boy
Have proved themselves top favourites here in our trials. Fruit have the shape and size of Marmande tomatoes with thick walls. Seed core is very small and taste is like a very sweet and juicy pepper. Very productrive plants. Top Boy has red fruits and is the earliest to ripen. Ideal for growing in a greenhouse or polytunnel. (Suff)
SBS; SUFF

Top Girl
Gold-yellow fruit. (Suff)
SBS; SUFF

Plantain
Plantago spp.
Buckshorn Plantain
Plantago coronopus.
FUTU

Potato

Solanum tuberosum

Accent

First Early. 1991. Lifting just after Dunluce, in first trials it has produced shallow-eyed tubers which have been notable for their eating quality, with an excellent new potato flavour. The flesh is pale cream, waxy and firm after boiling. Accent continues to bulk up to produce a heavy crop and mature tubers show no cracking, even under drought conditions. (Mars)

MARS; MART; TUCK

Ailsa

Maincrop. 1894. Round oval, white, with cream-coloured flesh. Heavy yield of even tubers. Resistant to external damage, and highly resistant to blackleg. Susceptible to spraing and virus Y. (GPG)

McL; ROG; WEBS

Alcmaria

First Early. 1969. Oval, yellow. Heavy early yield. Resistant to golden eelworm and slugs. Some resistance to common scab. (GPG)

MART

Alhambra

Maincrop. 1986. Long, red, with waxy texture. High yield. Resistant to golden eelworm. Susceptible to leaf roll virus. (GPG)

McL

Alwara

Second Early. Date unknown. Red oval. Close waxy texture. Eelworm resistant. (Webs)

McL

Aminca

First Early. 1974. High yielding. (GPG)

McL; OGC

Arkula

First Early. 1982. Oval, white. Very high yielding early. Resistant to spraing. Susceptible to foliage and tuber blight, also blackleg. (GPG)

MART; WEBS

Arran Banner

Maincrop. 1927. White, round, with deep eyes. Heavy yield, but irregular shape and often hollow hearted. Susceptible to slugs. (GPG)

WEBS

Arran Comet
First Early. 1956. Oval, white, with waxy texture. High early yield. Some resistance to common scab. Susceptible to virus Y, spraing, and blight, but is usually lifted before blight attacks. (GPG)
CALL; HEND; TUCK; WEBS

Arran Consul
WEBS

Arran Peak
McL

Arran Pilot
First Early. 1930. Heavy crop early but matures too large with uneven tubers. Liable to fail from cut seed tubers. Resistant to common scab, drought, and spraing. Susceptible to external damage and virus Y. (GPG)
CALL; HEND; MART; McL; ROG; ROG; TUCK; WEBS

Arran Victory
Late Maincrop. 1918. Round, purple, with white, very floury flesh. Good cooking qualities. Heavy cropper that keeps well. Resistant to common scab. A favourite in Ireland where it thrives in the moist climate. (GPG)
McL; WEBS

Aura
McL

Avalanche
Second Early. Date unknown. Round oval, white, with white flesh. Very uniform tubers. (GPG)
WEBS

BF 15
McL

Baillie
Second Early. 1981. Round, white, with shallow eyes. Moderate to high yield of uniform tubers. Resistant to Blight. (GPG)
McL

Ballydoon
First Early. 1931. White, oval. (GPG)
McL

Balmoral
WEBS

Potato

Belle de Fontenay
Early. Date unknown. For the very first salad potatoes. An extremely old French variety, which is still grown because of its exceptional culinary qualities. Small smooth kidney-shaped tubers with deep yellow flesh. Compact foliage. (Mars)
MARS; McL

Berber
Early Maincrop. Date unknown. White, round. High yield, stores well. A good all round variety, waxy. Eelworm resistant. (Webs)
McL

Berolina
McL

Bintje
Maincrop. 1910. Oval, white. Yellow flesh, high dry matter, resists drought, susceptible to blight and scab. Outclassed by Record, which is scab resisting. (GPG)
BAKK

Bishop
McL

Blue Catriona
Second Early. Date unknown. Long blue. Exhibition. (Webs)
McL

Bonnie Dundee
McL

British Queen
Second Early. 1894. Oval, white, with shallow eyes and white, floury flesh. Boils to mash if overcooked. Crops well. Resistant to slugs. Susceptible to blight and wart disease. (GPG)
McL; WEBS

Brodick
WEBS

Bute Blue
McL

Cara
Late Maincrop. 1976. Oval, pink, with shallow eyes and floury, white flesh. Ideal for jacket baking. High yield of uniform tubers. Late foliage maturity. Like a better-tempered King Edward. Resistant to blight, golden eelworm and virus Y. Some resistance to blackleg. Susceptible to powdery scab, gangrene and slugs. (GPG)
CALL; HEND; MARS; MART; McL; OGC; ROG; ROG; TUCK; WEBS

Cardinal
McL

Carlingford
Second Early. 1982. Round oval, white. (GPG)
McL; Tuck; Webs

Catriona
Second Early. 1920. Long oval, purple, with white, floury flesh. Low growing foliage which can be good for windy sites. Heavy cropper, haulm dies down early enough to miss blight and be lifted well before the worst slug attack. (GPG)
Call; Call; Hend; Mart; McL; Rog; Rog; Tuck; Webs

Champion
McL

Charlotte
Second Early. Date unknown. Developed in France during the 1980s to give tubers 50% bigger than other salad varieties. The crop is very uniform, shallow-eyed, long-oval in shape. The tender creamy-yellow flesh remains very firm and does not blacken on cooking. The excellent flavour—perhaps not quite as fine as Ratte—coupled with ease of culture ensures Charlotte's place in the first rank of potatoes for the connoisseur. (Mars)
Mars; McL; Tuck

Civa
McL

Cleopatra
Rog; Tuck

Concorde
Very early giving a heavy crop of quite large, long-oval tubers with shallow eyes. Has quickly become a popular show potato. The pale yellow flesh is firm and waxy in texture with exceptional flavour. Suitable for all soil types and quite resistant to late frosts. (Mars)
Mars; Mart; Tuck

Concurrent
First Early. Date unknown. White, oval, cream fleshed variety. Good drought resistance. (Scot)
Webs

Corine
McL

Cornes de Bique
McL

Potato

Costella
Second Early. Date unknown. Round oval, white, with yellow flesh. A good all round variety produces a heavy crop. Eelworm resistant. (Webs)
McL; Webs

Cromwell
McL

Cultra
Webs

Desiree
Maincrop. 1962. Long oval, red, with pale yellow, waxy flesh. Good for chips and baking. High yields but can get misshapen tubers on heavy soils. Crops well in drought, better than any other variety, even in 1976. Resistant to virus Y. Susceptible to mild mosaic virus, and very susceptible to common scab. Save your first lawn-mowings to put in the trenches against scab. (GPG)
Call; Dob; Hend; Mart; OGC; Rog; Rog; Tuck; Webs

Di Vernon
First Early. 1922. Oval, white skin, purple eyes. A very heavy cropper and a good cooker, floury flesh. (GPG)
McL; Webs

Diamant
Maincrop. 1982. Oval, white, with non-floury texture. Resistant to blight. (GPG)
McL

Diana
Maincrop. 1982. Round oval, red. Heavy yield of large, uniform tubers. Early foliage maturity. Some resistance to blackleg. Susceptible to external damage and bruising. (GPG)
Webs

Doon Pearl
McL

Doon Star
Webs

Dr McIntosh
Maincrop. 1944. Long, white. Susceptible to blight and drought. Shallow eyes, slow in dry seasons, flavour only moderate. (GPG)
McL

Duke Of York
First Early. 1891. Oval, white, with yellow floury flesh. Good for baking. Moderate yields of small tubers but can be left to grow large for storing. Susceptible to blight, wart disease and drought. (GPG)
CALL; HEND; MART; McL; ROG; ROG; TUCK; WEBS

Dunbar Rover
WEBS

Dunbar Standard
Late Maincrop. 1936. Long oval, white, with shallow eyes. Good keeper and cooker, excellent for chips, but tendency to after-cooking blackening. Liable to fail if tubers are cut. Late maturing, the haulm goes down in October. (GPG)
McL; TUCK; WEBS

Dunluce
First Early. 1976. Oval, white, with firm, cream flesh. Ideal for salad. Perhaps the earliest early of all, good for greenhouse forcing. Susceptible to blight and drought. (GPG)
MARS; TUCK; WEBS

Edgecote Purple
Cropping unknown. Date unknown. A smooth skinned purple kidney with shallow eyes. (Webs)
McL

Edzell Blue
Second Early. 1890. Round oval, purple blue, with white, floury flesh. Knobbly tubers, excellent roasted or steamed. (GPG)
McL; TUCK; WEBS

Epicure
First Early. 1897. Round, white, with deep eyes. High early yield. Tends to fail from cut seed. Good frost resistance. Susceptible to blight and wart disease. (GPG)
CALL; HEND; MART; McL; TUCK; WEBS

Estima
Second Early. 1937. Oval, white, with yellow, slightly waxy flesh. Good cooking and keeping qualities. Heavy crop particularly at later lifts. Resistant to blight, slugs and drought. Very susceptible to blackleg. Susceptible to powdery scab, virus Y and spraing. (GPG)
CALL; HEND; MART; ROG; ROG; TUCK; WEBS

Etoile Du Nord
McL

Potato

Fanfare
Early Maincrop. Date unknown. Round oval, pink. Exhibition. (Webs)
McL

Figaro
WEBS

Foremost
First Early. 1954. Oval, white with waxy, yellow flesh. Good cooker. Moderate yield. Poor foliage cover. Some slug resistance. (GPG)
CALL; HEND; MARS; MART; ROG; ROG; SUTT; TUCK; WEBS

Fortyfold
McL

Foxton
Maincrop. 1981. Oval, red-skin with light yellow flesh, firm floury texture. Excellent for roasting but some disintegration on boiling. (Seed)
McL

Fronika
Second Early. Date unknown. Round, red, waxy fleshed. Eelworm resistant. (Scot)
McL

Gladstone
McL

Golden Wonder
Late Maincrop. 1906. Long, russet, with floury, yellow flesh. Good baker, tends to disintegrate on boiling. Low yield of small tubers and does not thrive on all soils, suits the humid Irish climate best. Resistant to common scab. Susceptible to slug damage and drought. (GPG)
CALL; HEND; McL; ROG; ROG; TUCK; WEBS

Gracia
McL

Home Guard
First Early. 1942. Oval, white, with waxy flesh. Prone to blackening after cooking. Sprouts fast and bulks early. Resistant to external damage. Susceptible to drought and blight. Picks up any taint such as BHC from the soil, an organic gardener's potato. (GPG)
CALL; HEND; MART; ROG; ROG; TUCK; WEBS

Kennebec
Maincrop. 1963. Oval, white. Moderate to high yield, large tubers, close foliage cover. Susceptible to wart disease. (GPG)
WEBS

Kepplestone Kidney
Early Maincrop. Date unknown. Round, pink. A top show variety in very short supply. (Webs)
   McL

Kerr's Pink
Late Maincrop. 1917. Round, pink, with floury, cream flesh. Ideal for chips and does not blacken left cut up without water. Tendency to discolour and disintegrate with boiling. A late maturing, high yielder with a compact haulm that suppresses weeds. Quite susceptible to blight and scab. (GPG)
   CALL; HEND; McL; ROG; ROG; TUCK; WEBS

Kestrel
   MART; McL; TUCK; WEBS

King Edward
Maincrop. 1902. Long oval, pink and white, with floury, cream flesh. Good jacket potato. Famous for yield and quality, but only on soils it suits. Needs deep cultivation and was always a farm rather than a garden variety. Cut seed often fails. Susceptible to blight, wart disease, virus Y and drought. (GPG)
   CALL; HEND; MART; McL; ROG; ROG; TUCK; WEBS

King George
   McL

Kingston
Late Maincrop. 1981. Oval, white, with floury texture. Good jacket-baked. High yielding. Golden eelworm resistant. Susceptible to blight. (GPG)
   McL; WEBS

Kipfler
   McL

Kirsty
Maincrop. 1982. Round, white, with shallow eyes and creamy flesh. Excellent for jacket baking and creaming. High yield, medium sized tubers. Late foliage maturity. Some resistance to blackleg. Susceptible to spraing. HDRA members report that this variety can be very susceptible to slug damage. (GPG)
   MARS; ROG; TUCK; WEBS

Kondor
Maincrop. 1984. Oval, red, with yellow, creamy flesh that stays firm when boiled. High yielding Dutch variety with very large tubers. Blight resistant. (GPG)
   MARS; MART; TUCK

Potato

Linzer Delikatess
Early. 1975. The soft yellow salad potato preferred by the Austrians. Bred in Linz in 1975, it has only just been registered for sale in Britain. It produces large numbers of medium-sized, long-oval potatoes, with superficial eyes. Delicious hot or cold. (Mars)
MARS

Lola
First Early. 1981. Long oval, white, with pale yellow waxy flesh. No discoloration. Earlier and heavier cropping than Maris Bard. Resistant to common scab and virus Y. Susceptible to tuber blight. (GPG)
MARS

Majestic
CALL; HEND; MART; McL; ROG; ROG; TUCK; WEBS

Manna
First Early. 1977. Oval, white, with shallow eyes and waxy flesh. Heavy early crop. Susceptible to blight and blackleg. (GPG)
TUCK

Marfona
Second Early. 1977. Round, white. Dutch variety, excellent for baking. Heavy yield, large tubers, good foliage cover. Good on light soils. Good overall disease resistance, including some to blackleg. (GPG)
MARS; MART; McL; ROG; TUCK; WEBS

Maris Bard
First Early. 1972. Long oval, white, with waxy flesh. Very early and high yielding, sprouts relatively late. Good forced under glass. Susceptible to powdery scab and blackleg. (GPG)
CALL; DOB; HEND; MARS; MART; ROG; ROG; TUCK; WEBS

Maris Peer
Second Early. 1962. Round oval, white, with waxy flesh. Moderate yield, plentiful small tubers, used for canned new potatoes. Early sprouter. Resistant to common scab and skin spot. Susceptible to drought. (GPG)
CALL; HEND; MART; TUCK; WEBS

Maris Piper
Maincrop. 1963. Oval, white, with floury flesh. Good baker. High yield, large number tubers per plant. Eelworm (golden) resistant and some resistance to blackleg. Susceptible to common and powdery scab, drought, and slugs. (GPG)
DOB; HEND; MART; McL; ROG; ROG; TUCK; WEBS

Mauve Queen
McL

May Queen
McL

Mona Lisa
McL

Montana
McL

Morag
Early Maincrop. 1985. Oval, white. Moderate yield. Resistant to leaf roll virus. Partial resistance to both golden and pale eelworm. Susceptible to virus Y and tuber blight. (GPG)
WEBS

Morene
Second Early. 1983. Round, white. High yield, large tubers. Resistant to common scab and golden eelworm. Susceptible to wart disease, gangrene and virus Y. Very susceptible to blackleg. (GPG)
McL; OGC

Nadine
The housewife's choice. Lots of uniform-sized round tubers, strongly resistant to eelworm. The skin is exceptionally smooth with shallow eyes, perfect for showing. The sweet white flesh remains firm and moist on cooking. (Mars)
CALL; DOB; HEND; MARS; MART; McL; ROG; ROG; TUCK; WEBS

Navan
Maincrop. Date unknown. Excellent white round-oval. Floury, firm flesh. Good for showing. Eelworm resistant.
WEBS

Palma
McL

Penta
Second Early. 1983. Round, pink-eyed, with yellow flesh. High yield, large tubers. Resistant to external damage. Susceptible to leaf roll virus, powdery scab. (GPG)
McL; WEBS

Pentland Crown
Maincrop. 1958. Oval, white, with waxy flesh. Tendency to blackening after cooking. Very high yielder. Can be rather tasteless, but improves after Christmas. A supermarket suppliers' favourite. Resistant to common scab, leaf roll virus, virus Y. Some resistance to blackleg. Susceptible to slugs, powdery scab, spraing. (GPG)
CALL; HEND; MART; ROG; ROG; TUCK; WEBS

Potato

Pentland Dell
Late Maincrop. 1960. Long oval, white, with floury texture. Good for baking and roasting but tendency to blacken, and to disintegrate on boiling. High yielder. Very susceptible to tuber blight and spraing. (GPG)
    CALL; HEND; ROG; ROG; TUCK; WEBS

Pentland Hawk
Maincrop. 1967. Oval, white, with waxy flesh. Good in salads. Moderate to high yields, long keeper. Susceptible to virus Y and spraing. (GPG)
    CALL; HEND; ROG; WEBS

Pentland Ivory
Maincrop. 1966. Round oval, white, with floury texture. High yield of large, shapely tubers. Some resistance to tuber blight and common scab. Resistant to virus Y. Susceptible to spraing. (GPG)
    CALL; ROG; WEBS

Pentland Javelin
First Early. 1968. Oval, white, with very white, waxy flesh. Slow sprouting, bulks late. Resistant to golden eelworm, virus Y and common scab. Susceptible to spraing. (GPG)
    CALL; HEND; MART; ROG; ROG; TUCK; WEBS

Pentland Lustre
    TUCK; WEBS

Pentland Squire
Maincrop. 1970. Oval, white. High yield of large tubers if on fertile soil. Prone to hollow heart, so needs high seed rate to prevent tubers getting too big. Some resistance to blight and blackleg. (GPG)
    CALL; HEND; ROG; ROG; WEBS

Pimpernel
    McL

Pink Fir Apple
Late Maincrop. 1880. Long, pink, with yellow, waxy flesh. Salad potatoes, remaining firm when diced cold, appreciated in France where they make the real "French Fried". Low yield, unusual shaped tubers. (GPG)
    CALL; HEND; MARS; MART; McL; ROG; ROG; SMM; TUCK; WEBS

Premier
    TUCK; WEBS

Pride Of Bute
McL

Promesse
McL

Provost
First Early. 1981. Oval, white. Good foliage cover. (GPG)
McL

Ratte
Second Early. 1972. Long, white, with yellow, waxy flesh. Ideal for salad and boiling. Grown in France since 1972 as a higher yielding alternative to Pink Fir Apple. (GPG)
MARS; McL; WEBS

Record
Maincrop. 1944. Oval, white, with yellow floury flesh. The highest dry matter potato, mainly grown on contract for potato crisps. Moderate to low yield. Resists blight, spraing and common scab. Susceptible to virus Y, blackleg, drought and internal bruising. (GPG)
CALL; HEND; McL; ROG; WEBS

Red Cara
Late Maincrop. Date unknown. Round oval, red, waxy. Eelworm resistant. (Webs)
WEBS

Red Craigs Royal
Second Early. 1957. Oval, pink, with shallow eyes and floury flesh. Excellent for potato salad, remaining firm when diced cold, as good as Pink Fir Apple, but a vastly greater yield. The only way to enjoy the old Craig's Royal flavour. Moderate yield, tubers large if left to grow. A good keeper. Resistant to powdery scab. Susceptible to external damage and hair cracking. (GPG)
ROG; ROG; TUCK; WEBS

Red Duke of York
First Early. 1942. Oval, red, with floury flesh. Good for baking. The flavour, keeping and floury baking qualities of the old white skinned favourite, combined with good exhibition colour. (GPG)
BAKK; CALL; HEND; MART; McL; TUCK; WEBS

Red King Edward
Maincrop. 1916. Long oval, red, with floury texture. Good general cooking qualities. Moderate yield, large number of tubers per plant. Differs only in colour from the original. Resistant to common scab. Susceptible to wart disease, blight, virus Y and drought. (GPG)
McL

Potato

Red Pontiac
Maincrop. 1985. Round, red, with waxy flesh. Excellent jacket baked. An American variety. (Webs)
> WEBS

Red Stormont 480
> McL

Rocket
Just as early as Dunluce, it has pure white flesh, which is waxy and soft at first digging. Even sized tubers, a little larger than a hen's egg. (Mars)
> MARS; MART; McL; ROG; TUCK; WEBS

Rode Eerstelling see Red Duke of York
Romano
Maincrop. 1978. Round oval, red. White flesh with a creamy texture. Stays firm on cooking. Moderate to high yields. Resistant to virus Y. Some resistance to blight and blackleg. Susceptible to leaf roll virus and drought. Like an earlier, less scab likely Desiree. (GPG)
> CALL; HEND; MARS; MART; ROG; ROG; TUCK; WEBS

Royal Kidney
Second Early. 1899. Long oval, white, with yellow flesh. Keeps if left to grow large. Fine flavour. Susceptible to wart disease. (GPG)
> McL; WEBS

Russet Conference
> McL

Ryecroft Purple
> McL

Salad Blue
Second Early. Date unknown. Novelty blue flesh. (Webs)
> McL

Salad Red
> McL

Samba
Long and oval in shape, white skinned with a creamy flesh. (Tuck)
> TUCK

Sante
Maincrop. 1983. Round oval, white, with shallow eyes and cream coloured, floury flesh. High yield of uniform tubers. Good all-round disease resistance, including resistance to golden eelworm, and partial resistance to pale eelworm. Some susceptibility to blackleg and gangrene. (GPG)
CALL; MARS; WEBS

Seaforde
McL

Sharpe's Express
First Early. 1901. Long, white, with yellow, floury flesh. Ideal baker, but goes to mash if overcooked. Moderate to low yield, large number of tubers per plant. Keeps well. Like Duke of York, grown as an early for scraping and a second early for keeping. Susceptible to tuber blight and wart disease. (GPG)
CALL; HEND; MART; McL; ROG; ROG; TUCK; WEBS

Shula
Cropping unknown. Date unknown. Pink splashed oval white. Great for showing. Excellent long keeping firm fleshed variety. The best for baking or microwave use. (Scot)
ROG; WEBS

Stamina
WEBS

Stemster
Maincrop. 1986. Long oval, pink, with light yellow flesh. High yield, large tubers. Golden eelworm and slug resistant. Excellent exhibition. (GPG)
CALL; HEND; MART; WEBS

Stormont Star
McL

Stroma
Second Early. Date unknown. Oval, light yellow, with pale yellow flesh. Some slug resistance. (GPG)
HEND; MART; ROG; SUTT; WEBS

Sutton's Foremost see Foremost
Swift
McL

Ukama
McL

Potato

Ulster Chieftain
First Early. 1938. Oval, white. An excellent early roaster. Has short haulm so does well on wind-swept sites and grows fast early, with a better crop than Arran Pilot by the end of June. Susceptible to blight, scab and frost damage. (GPG)
CALL; HEND; MART; McL; ROG; ROG; TUCK; WEBS

Ulster Classic
McL

Ulster Prince
First Early. 1947. Long, white, with waxy flesh. Produces few tubers per plant. Emergence often slow and irregular. Forces well under glass. Resists drought. Susceptible to frost damage and very susceptible to spraing. (GPG)
ROG; WEBS

Ulster Sceptre
First Early. 1964. Long, white. High yielder on fertile soil. Very early and high yielding, sprouts rapidly. Drought resistant. Poor virus resistance. Seed susceptible to mechanical damage and gangrene. (GPG)
ROG; ROG; TUCK; WEBS

Ulster Sovereign
McL

Up-to-Date
Late Maincrop. 1894. Oval, white. Moderate yields, good keeper. Drought resistant. Susceptible to blight, common scab and wart disease. (GPG)
McL; WEBS

Urgenta
Early. Date unknown, pre 1981. Oval, red skin, yellow flesh, shallow eyes, heavy yields, excellent cooking quality and flavour. Dutch variety. (GSI)
McL

Valor
WEBS

Vanessa
CALL; HEND; MART; McL

Verena
McL

Wilja
Second Early. 1972. Long, white with yellow, waxy flesh. Good for potato salads. High yield with large number of tubers per plant. Blight resistant, and some resistance to common scab and blackleg. Susceptible to virus Y. (GPG)
CALL; DOB; HEND; MART; OGC; ROG; ROG; TUCK; WEBS

Winston
MART; WEBS

Witchhill
McL

Purslane

Portulaca spp
Grown for salad leaves in summer.

Common
A succulent continental salad herb. Sow outside in spring, watering well at seeding stage. (Poyn)
CHAM; POYN

Golden
Attractive yellow leaves. Rather rare. (Suff)
SUFF

Green
Well flavoured and vigorous. Pick over a long season. (Suff)
BAKK; FUTU; SBS; SUFF

Pink
Montia sibirica. An attractive annual with glossy green leaves and pretty pink flowers. A native of North America that is commonly naturalised, Pink Purslane grows well in moist and shady places. The pleasantly flavoured leaves can be eaten as a salad or cooked. (Futu)
FUTU

Yellow
CHAM; SBS

Quinoa

Chenopodium quinoa
An annual from the high Andes, slowly emerging from the plots of enthusiasts to more general acceptance. It is related to Fat Hen, and is as easy to grow. In summer, the plants develop large seedheads that are loaded with millet-sized seeds that thresh easily. The seeds are coated with bitter protective substances, which must be removed by washing and rubbing, but the grain can then be cooked as rice or ground into flour. The seeds are very nutritious.

Cahuil
Medium sized light green seeds, a reliable producer. (Futu)
FUTU

Radish

Dave
Medium sized yellow-brown seeds, a very short season variety. (Futu)
FUTU

Faro
Has small white seeds, the most productive of 16 varieties. (Futu)
FUTU

Isluga Yellow
Medium sized yellow seed. Early maturing and high yielding. (Futu)
FUTU

Radish
Raphanus sativus
Storage radishes, also known as winter radishes, have much larger roots that keep well.

18 Day
Fast "French Breakfast" which is crisp with a mild sweet flavour. Has long white tipped scarlet roots. (Suff)
SUFF

Beacon
SBS

Bisai Japanese Seedling
Young leaves used as a cut and come again seedling crop. Specially selected variety for rapid leaf growth. Sow broadcast from spring until autumn. Harvest when 10-20 cm. high after approx 25-35 days. (Suff)
OGC

Bison
JOHN

Bonella
SBS

F1 Briljant
MOLE

Carvella
SBS

Cello
SBS

F1 Cherokee
DOB; JOHN; T&M

Cherry Belle
Excellent variety for spring and summer cultivation outdoors. Beautiful colour. Flesh stays deliciously crisp. (Bakk)
BAKK; BREE; BRWN; CGAR; D&D; DOB; EWK; JOHN; JWB; MARS; MOLE; OGC; ROG; SBS; SUFF; T&M; TUCK; UNWI; VANH; WALL; YATE

Crimson Giant
SBS

Crystal Ball
Slow to go pithy. Roots remain firm and crisp when other varieties have gone pithy. (Toze)
SUTT; TOZE

F1 Cyros
EWK; SBS; YATE

D'Avignon
Longest French variety with delicate crunchy flesh with a touch of fire. Very pretty too with intense rose colour and a white tip. Up to 3 in. long. (Suff)
SUFF

F1 Durabel
BAKK

Easter Egg
Round radish that comes in four different colours. Red, pink, purple and white. Ready to pick early and they stay crisp and mild even when large. Great fun for children to grow. Best grown in cool weather. (Suff)
SUFF

Fire Candle
Smooth skinned red variety grows up to 6 in. in length. Ideal for slicing with a strong flavour. Sow from July onwards. (OGC)
OGC

Flair
MOLE

Flamboyant
BREE

F1 Fluo
FOTH

F1 Flyer
SBS

Fota
SBS

Radish

French Breakfast
Mild flavoured, crisp and tender. Long-rooted, red with a white tip and tail. (Foth)
> BAKK; CGAR; CHIL; D&D; EWK; FOTH; JOHN; JWB; MARS; MOLE; OGC; ROG; SBS; SMM; TOZE; TUCK; VANH; WALL

French Breakfast 3
Solid, sweet, cylindrical crimson and white roots. (Sutt)
> BRWN; CART; DOB; SUTT; T&M; UNWI

French Breakfast Forcing
> MOLE; SBS

French Breakfast Fusilier
An early stock of this popular variety suitable for forcing. (Brwn)
> BRWN; JOHN; SBS; YATE

French Breakfast Lanquette
> RSLU

French Breakfast Large White Tipped
> SBS

Gaudry
Suitable for sowing in the open as well as under glass. A delicious variety, much used for garnishing salads. One of the most widely grown Continental radish varieties. (Bakk)
> BAKK

Globe Varieties Mixed
A mixture of red, pink, white and bi-coloured radishes. Globe-shaped, crisp and of a good flavour. (Unwi)
> UNWI

Helro
Very high quality round roots of intense red. Suitable for outdoor production and protected cropping. (Toze)
> JOHN; SBS

F1 Juliette
> T&M

Karissima
> YATE

Long White Icicle
Long-rooted, crisp, tender with a mild flavour and white tips. A change from usual reds. (Foth)
> BAKK; BRWN; CGAR; D&D; DOB; EWK; FOTH; JOHN; JWB; MARS; MOLE; OGC; ROG; SBS; SUTT; TUCK; UNWI; VANH; WALL

F1 Mantanghong
JOHN; SUTT; T&M

Misato Green
Similar to Misato Red but green all through. (OGC)
OGC

Misato Red
Large turnip shaped roots about 10cm in diameter. Toots keep for a long time after harvest. The tender sweet flesh is pink with white flecks making an interesting addition to salads. Sow July onwards. (OGC)
OGC; SUFF

Misato Rose
EWK; SBS; WALL

Novired
RSLU

Parat
Can be left to grow to enormous size without going pithy or splitting. Roots are round, attractive carmine-red and have a mild flavour. (Foth)
FOTH

Pegaso
MOLE

Pink Beauty
Of unique colouring and subtle flavour. Attractive, pink, globe-shaped roots are very uniform in size and of first-rate quality. (Dob)
DOB; JOHN; SUTT

Poker
SBS

Pontvil
Beautiful French Breakfast-type that overcomes that frustrating feature of this shape of radish going hollow, hot and woolly so quickly after maturing. Stays crisp, sweet and firm longer. (T&M)
T&M

Primella
SBS

Prinz Rotin
Fine scarlet globe, which keeps crisp and does not go pithy when quite large, up to 1.5 in. across if sown thinly. (Mars)
BRWN; FOTH; MARS; SBS; T&M; UNWI

Radish

Revosa
Small round scarlet roots which mature very rapidly. A popular variety which will stay solid for a long time. Very uniform and of excellent flavour. Not suitable for sowing under glass. (VanH)
VanH

Ribella
Very fast growing, for earliest crops of outdoor radish. Also for cold frames, cloches, etc. Beautiful, round, bright-red roots, slow to become pithy. Sow from February onwards. (Mars)
Mars

Riesenbutter
King-sized radish with flesh as soft as butter. Slow in getting spongy. Fast grower that can be grown successfully by every home gardener. (Bakk)
Bakk

F1 Rondar
Bree

Ronde Rode see Round Red Forcing

Rota
Deep red radish which remains firm and crisp even when oversize. Excellent both for under glass and outside cropping. (OGC)
John; Mole; OGC; SbS

Round Red Forcing
Red, white tipped, crisp, quick growing radish. Contiuous sowings throughout spring and summer. (VanH)
VanH

Round Red Forcing Real
SbS

Round Red Outdoor Gala
Round red large rooted radish, with good resistance against sponginess and a deep red colour. (Bree)
Bree

Rudi
Yate

Saxa
Standard variety, guaranteed to give a high yield of bright red radishes. Advisable to sow Saxa in the open. (Bakk)
Bakk; John; JWB; Mole; SbS; Toze

Saxa Nova
Round red variety for summer production under glass as well as outdoors. (Bree)
BREE

Scarlet Globe
Excellent shaped round roots, quick growing and very pungent. Can be sown early in cold frames. (EWK)
CART; CGAR; CHIL; D&D; EWK; FOTH; JOHN; MOLE; OGC; ROG; SBS; SMM; SUTT; WALL

Scharo
MOLE; SBS

Short Top Forcing
For sowing during October-February in a cold frame, greenhouse or under cloches. A fine round, bright scarlet radish which holds its colour and retains its quality when grown under protection. (Dob)
DOB; SUTT

F1 Solar
BREE

Sparkler
Very uniform globe type with brighter red skin and white tip. (EWK)
EWK

Sparkler 3
Medium-sized, round red roots tipped with white. (Sutt)
CGAR; D&D; DOB; JOHN; JWB; OGC; ROG; SBS; SUTT; VANH; WALL

F1 Speedar
BREE

Summer Crunch
A brand new introduction of the French Breakfast type. Long stump ended roots of deep pink colour with very small white tip. Really crisp, sweet tasting white flesh. (Suff)
EWK; SUFF

Summerred
RSLU

Volcano
Our new introduction of the semi-long type. Superb quality roots with scarlet skin and very small white tip. Crisp white pungent flesh for early forcing or maincrop production. (EWK)
CGAR; EWK; ROG; SBS

White Hailstone
SBS

White Turnip
SBS

Woods Frame
SBS

Radish Storage

F1 April Cross
BAKK; FOTH; JOHN; MARS; T&M; TOZE; UNWI; YATE

Black Spanish
Spicy and hot for autumn and winter use. (CGar)
CGAR

Black Spanish Long
Long black roots with white flesh, spicy and hot. (OGC)
BAKK; CHIL; EWK; JOHN; OGC; SBS; SUFF

Black Spanish Round
Very hardy with white flesh of good flavour. (Dob)
BRWN; D&D; DOB; EWK; FUTU; JOHN; JWB; OGC; ROG; SBS; SUFF; SUTT; TUCK; VANH; WALL

China Rose
Good flavoured longer roots with white flesh. Sow in the autumn. (D&D)
CGAR; D&D; EWK; FOTH; JOHN; JWB; MOLE; OGC; ROG; SBS; SUFF; SUTT; TUCK; UNWI; WALL

F1 Easter
YATE

Mino Early
A large Japanese variety for use, thinly sliced, in autumn and winter salads. The roots, about 15 in. long and 2 in. in diameter are very mild in flavour. (Dob)
DOB; JOHN; SUTT

F1 Minowase
EWK; JWB; OGC; SUFF; TUCK; YATE

F1 Minowase 2
CGAR; JOHN; WALL

F1 Minowase No 1
SBS

Minowase Summer
   D&D; Rog

Mooli
Not a variety name, but a general term for a long, white radish.
   EWK

Munchen Bier
Grown for its tasty seed pods. Leave to grow and it will flower very quickly. Spicy pods for eating raw or lightly cooked. (EWK)
   EWK; OGC; SbS; Suff

Ostergruss rosa
Pungent and highly aromatic variety. Does not become spongy. Sow from April onwards. (Bakk)
   Bakk

Rex
Very bolt-resistant variety. Therefore, it can be sown fairly early. Suitable for growing under glass as well as in the open. (Bakk)
   Bakk

Robino
   John; SbS

F1 Silverstar
   Bakk

Rampion

Campanula rapunculus
Although not widely grown, the roots of this biennial native plant are fleshy and good raw or cooked. The plot of the fairy story Rapunzel hangs on rampions being stolen from the magician's garden.

Rampion
   Chil; Futu; Suff

Rape

Brassica napus
Usually grown as the cress in mustard and cress.

Broad Leaf Essex
May be used instead of mustard and cress and as a sprouting seed. Sown outside makes a good cut and come again crop. (Suff)
   Mole; SbS; Suff; Wall

Emerald
MAS

Giant English
Popular in salads in place of mustard, milder flavour. (JWB)
JWB; MAS

Salad Rape
The old traditional "Mustard and Cress". Quick growing with excellent flavour. Sow inside in containers or direct into open ground. Make frequent sowings for continuous cutting. Ready in 10 days. (EWK)
BRWN; CHIL; EWK; JOHN; OGC

Rhubarb

Rheum rhabarbarum

Champagne Early see Early Red

Early Red
(Champagne Early.) Long, bright scarlet stalks of good flavour. Some of the plants will be exceptionally early. (Unwi)
MARS; UNWI

Glaskin's Perpetual
The one variety that can be cut in the first year of sowing. To do so, it is essential to get it off to an early start and keep it growing throughout the season. (OGC)
CHIL; DOB; EWK; JOHN; JWB; MOLE; OGC; ROG; SBS; SMM; SUFF; T&M; TUCK; VANH; WALL

Holstein Blood Red
A vigorous grower, producing juicy dark blood-red stalks. (Dob)
SBS

Large Victoria
SBS

Prince Albert
SBS

Redstick
JWB; SBS

Strawberry
SBS

Timperley Early
Ideally plant February-March, but any time from October-January can succeed if soil conditions allow. This variety is suitable for forcing and produces thin, tasty stalks. (Tuck)
> TUCK

Victoria
Much easier than you think to grow your own rhubarb from seed and so satisfying with this excellent variety. (Foth)
> BRWN; FOTH; JOHN; MOLE; SBS; SUTT; WALL

Rock Samphire
Crithmum maritimum
A hardy perennial with glaucous divided leaves and umbels of yellow flowers. A native of sea cliffs of Britain, so it should do well planted in crevices in walls and in rock gardens. The salty leaves have an aromatic smell somewhat reminiscent of lemon curd, and can be used as a garnish, in salads, pickled, or steamed and eaten with butter.

Rock Samphire
Yellow-white flowers and succulent foliage which is excellent to eat either fresh, cooked or pickled. (Poyn)
> FUTU; POYN

Rocket
Eruca sativa
Excellent in salads, it is doubtful that there are any true varieties.

Rocket
Biennial, 2 ft., full sun. Mustard flavoured leaves excellent in salads. (D&D)
> CGAR; CHIL; D&D; EWK; FUTU; POYN; SBS; SUTT

Rucola
Can be sown in rows in April or May, keeping the rows at least 18 in. apart. The tender young leaves are used in salads as an addition to lettuce or endive. (OGC)
> OGC

Salad Rocket
This is a superb salad vegetable with leaves of a delicious rich spicy flavour. Quite unlike anything else. Sow any time from February to September for an almost all year round supply. Very simple to grow and practically no pests or diseases. If you haven't a garden you can grow it in a pot on a window sill or include in a mustard and cress mix. An easy tasty crop that really ought to be better known. (Suff)
> SUFF

Rocket Turkish
Bunias orientalis
A hardy perrennial that produces large quantities of leaves which, when young and tender, are eaten in salads or boiled as greens. It starts into growth early in the spring, when there are few fresh vegetables about, and withstands cold and drought well.

Turkish Rocket
FUTU

Rosette Pak Choi
Brassica rapa var. rosularis
Also known as Tatsoi and Tasai, this type of Pak Choi forms a flattend head, rather like an endive.

F1 Ryokusai
T&M

Tatsoi
This is not a true variety name, but simply the Japanese for Rosette Pak Choi.
D&D; EWK; OGC; SBS; SMM; SUFF

Runner Bean
Phaseolus coccineus

Achievement
Outstanding variety for table or exhibition. Top quality long pods. (Mars)
BREE; JOHN; MARS; MOLE; ROG; RSLU; SUTT; TOZE; WALL

Bokki
ROG; YATE

Butler
This is a prolific cropper that is also completely stringless. Good sized tender pods on strong vigorous plants. Produces over a long period. (OGC)
CGAR; EWK; OGC; ROG; SUTT; WALL

Crusader
Produces fine long exhibition pods of good cooking quality. (Brwn)
BRWN; CGAR; EWK; FOTH; JOHN; JWB; ROG; SMM; UNWI; VANH

Czar
A white seeded type with long rather rough pods. Good flavour cooked green, if left to dry it will give a crop of "butter" beans. (OGC)
EWK; JOHN; OGC; ROG; SUFF; TUCK

Desiree
A white seeded variety that produces long slender, fleshy pods, at least 10ins in length. Exceptional flavour and stringless, it crops very heavily. 40 pods per plant can be expected. Suitable for freezing. (OGC)

CGar; D&D; EWK; Foth; John; JWB; Mars; OGC; Rog; SMM; T&M; VanH; Wall

Enorma
An improved Prizewinner type with long pods of excellent quality. (Brwn)

Bree; Brwn; CGar; Dob; EWK; Foth; John; Mars; MAS; Mole; Rog; RSlu; SbS; Shar; SMM; Sutt; T&M; Toze; Tuck; Wall; Yate

Fry Stringo
Bree

Gulliver
High quality stringless runner bean on non-climbing plants approx. 12ins. No need for staking. Long straight smooth 9-10in. pods. Self-stopping, early, high yielding, difficult for exposed gardens needs cloches. (T&M)

Cart; Dob; Rog; T&M; Toze

Hammonds Dwarf Scarlet
A bush runner bean for the smaller garden, tops may need to be pinched out to stop running. Easy to pick and and no poles needed. (OGC)

CGar; D&D; EWK; JWB; OGC; Rog; SMM; Unwi; VanH; Wall

Ivanhoe
A quality early variety with long straight fleshy and thick up to 18in. pods which are stringless when young and reasonably so when mature. Scarlet flowers, unique lilac pink seeds. Recommended for exhibition. Early, high yielding. (T&M)

T&M

Kelvedon Marvel
Reading for picking ten days earlier than other varieties. A heavy cropper it is deservedly popular with both gardeners and growers. (OGC)

Bree; Brwn; CGar; D&D; EWK; John; JWB; Mars; Mole; OGC; Rog; RSlu; SbS; Toze; Unwi; Wall

Lady Di
Producing extra long and slender pods with a smooth skin and very slow to develop seed. Well worth a try. (OGC)

Brwn; CGar; D&D; EWK; Foth; John; OGC; Rog; T&M; Tuck; Unwi; VanH; Wall

Runner Bean

Liberty
Very smooth, thick flesh with a large number of beans per truss up to 35ins. in length. (JWB)
> CGar; JWB; Rob; Wall

Mergoles
White-flowered and white-seeded, with long, fleshy pods in abundance right through the autumn. One of the best to grow for freezing. (Foth)
> Bakk; Dob; Foth; Sutt

Painted Lady
(1855) Add colour to the vegetable garden with the attractive red and white blossoms. Grow in the herbaceous border or against and unsightly fence. (OGC)
> CGar; Dob; EWK; Foth; John; JWB; Mars; OGC; Rog; SMM; Suff; Tuck; Wall

Pickwick
(Unwi)
> Brwn; Foth; John; Mars; Sutt; Toze; Tuck; Unwi

Polestar
The scarlet flowers set easily and produce and abundant crop of 25cm long beans. Vigour is maintained throughout the season. In our opinion this one is simply the best stringless runner bean available. (Unwi)
> Foth; John; Mars; Mole; Sutt; Toze; Unwi; Wall

Prizetaker
Our own selected strain of outstanding quality. Good sized pods useful for freezing. (EWK)
> EWK; John; Rog; SbS

Prizewinner
Large fleshy pods of fine quality and good flavour. (Unwi)
> Cart; CGar; Chil; EWK; John; JWB; MAS; Rog; SbS; Shar; Sutt; Tuck; Unwi; VanH; Wall

Red Knight
Red flowered, this crops very heavily and the stringless beans are excellent for freezing. (OGC)
> Bree; Brwn; Cart; D&D; EWK; Foth; JWB; Mars; OGC; Rog; SMM; Suff; VanH; Wall

Red Rum
Very early with a tremendous yield of 6-8in. fleshy, almost stringless, well flavoured pods. The first variety we know with some resistance to halo blight. Seed saved from the hybrid will not breed true. Very heavy yield, very early - can be used as a ground bean. Organic gardeners. (T&M)
> T&M

Royal Standard
An impressive new variety. Smooth, bright green, fleshy, completely stringless, 20in. pods which are set well under adverse conditions. Early, heavy yielding. Exhibition. (T&M)
> Dob; T&M

Scarlet Emperor
(1906) A traditional variety that is as good today as when first introduced at the turn of the century. Preferred by many gardeners for its flavour. (OGC)
> Cart; CGar; D&D; Dob; EWK; Foth; John; OGC; Rog; SbS; Shar; Suff; Sutt; T&M; Unwi; VanH; Wall

Streamline
A Chase speciality. Good pods of great length as well as excellent texture and flavour. The shape and uniformity of pods makes this useful for the exhibitor. (OGC)
> Bakk; Brwn; Cart; CGar; Chil; Dob; EWK; John; JWB; Mars; Mole; OGC; Rog; RSlu; SbS; Shar; T&M; Toze; Tuck; Unwi; VanH; Wall; Yate

Sunset
> Sutt

White Achievement
> Sutt

White Emergo
White flowered and white seeded. Long slender pods of fine texture and fine flavour. Especially good for deep freezing. (Unwi)
> Bakk; Brwn; CGar; D&D; EWK; Foth; John; Mole; Rog; RSlu; SbS; Shar; Toze; Unwi; Wall; Yate

Salad Mallow
Malva crispa
A vigorous annual that reaches 1 m. or more and produces light green leaves with crinkled edges and pale pink flowers, making it an attractive plant. The leaves can be eaten in salads or stir-fried, and have excellent flavour and texture. Easily grown, with self-sown seedlings often surviving the winter.

Salad Mallow
> Futu

Salsify
Tragopogon porrifolium
Grown for its edible roots, which give it the name of Oyster Plant. It is doubtful that any of the varieties are truly distinct.

Giant
Called vegetable oyster because of its delicate, distinctive flavour. Long roots to be sliced and fried in butter, or boiled until tender. (Sutt)
SUTT

Mammoth
Long, tapering white roots which can be either boiled or fried. Of sweet, delicious flavour. (Mars)
MARS; UNWI

Salsify
An interesting root vegetable that may be baked like parsnip, pureed for soup, or just grated raw into salads. (Poyn)
CGAR; CHAM; FUTU; POYN

Sandwich Island
Long, white tapering roots of smooth texture for Winter use. (EWK)
CHIL; DOB; EWK; JOHN; JWB; OGC; ROG; SBS; SMM; SUFF; T&M; TUCK; WALL

Scorzonera
Scorzonera hispanica
Also known as Black Salsify, and also grown for the roots.

Black
CHAM

Duplex
Should not be sown too early, or it will form seed stalks. Harvest early Winter. Produces a good crop of long, unbranched roots. This variety is a real delicacy. Rich in vitamins. (Bakk)
BAKK

Giant Rooted
SBS

Habil
Long, straight, cylindrical roots with dark brown skin. Delicious sweet flavour somewhat similar to salsify. (Mars)
MARS

Lange Jan
Delicious when scraped and boiled in vinegar and salted water can be served like asparagus. Dark brown in colour, the roots are long and tapering. (Dob)
Dob; SbS; Unwi

Large Black
Another unusual and delicious vegetable looking not unlike salsify but with black-skinned roots. Easily raised, it can be grown and cooked like salsify. (Chil)
Chil

Long Black
The long roots should be scalded and cooked in salty water or sliced and fried in butter. Deliciously sweet flavour. (Foth)
Foth; John; JWB; SbS

Long John see Lange Jan
Maxima
Similar to salsify but with black roots. The small young leaves are eaten as salad. (OGC)
John; OGC; Rog; SbS; SMM; Tuck

Russian Giant
Black-skinned roots with unusual, delicate flavour. Scald and scrape before boiling in salted water; or slice, fry in butter, and serve garnished with parsley. (Sutt)
Sutt

Scorzonera
Cultural instructions as for salsify. Similar to salsify but with black skin. Reputed to deter carrot fly if sown with carrots. (Tuck)
D&D; EWK; Futu; Poyn; Suff; Wall

Sea Kale
Crambe maritima
A perennial that is a Brassica, not related to seakale beet. The blanched shoots make a delicious winter vegetable.

Lily White
A heavy cropper with well-flavoured shoots. (Futu)
Chil; Futu; SbS; SMM; Suff; T&M

Sea Kale
The long succulent blanched shoots are boiled and served like asparagus, with melted butter. Also can be eaten raw in salads. (Mars)
Cham; Mars; OGC; Pask; Poyn; WKi

Shallot

White
JOHN

Shallot
Allium cepa var. aggregatum

Atlantic
Very firm crisp and crunchy golden brown skinned shallots with an excellent flavour. They are early, producing higher yields of better quality than standard types and have very long storing capabilities. Autumn harvested shallots can easily be kept until late spring in a cool dry room. (T&M)

ROG; SUTT; T&M; UNWI

F1 Creation
The first hybrid shallot grown from seed. Yellow shallots with an extra mild flavour tasty for salads as well as for cooking. All the benefits of growing from seed - less risk of virus, bigger crop - and it doesn't bolt at all. Creation is very easy to grow, sow anytime from late February to late April, when the soil conditions are suitable. Matures late August, and will store as late as the following June without any problems. (Unwi)

CART; DOB; SUTT; T&M; UNWI

Delicato
Improved Red Shallot, with much better keeping qualities and less susceptible to virus. Strongly flavoured like the old Giant Red, the white flesh is attractively marked with pink rings. Large bulbs, with deep golden-brown skins. (Mars)

MARS

Dobies' Longkeeping Yellow
A reliable variety, crops well and keeps sound for months. Can be planted from February onwards. (Dob)

DOB

Dutch Red
ROG

Dutch Yellow
High yielding and easy to grow. (Unwi)

OGC; ROG; UNWI

Exhibition
SMM

Giant Yellow
Improved stock with better keeping quality. Each bulb planted will split to yield several shallots. Fine for salads or for pickling. (Mars)

MARS; SUTT

Golden Gourmet
New much improved yellow variety. Firm even shallots, store well. (Tuck)
D&D; EWK; John; OGC; Rog; Suff; Tuck

Hative de Niort
Classic exhibition shallot. Bulbs of excellent form, deep flask-shaped and uniform, circular cross-section. Deep brown skins. (Mars)
Dob; JWB; Mars; Sutt

Pikant
Very well flavoured red shallots with very long keeping qualities. They are very early and high yielding too. Each bulb divided into many shallots at harvest time. (T&M)
Mars; Rog; Sutt; T&M

Sante
Excellent for exhibition and kitchen use, producing large, round flavoursome bulbs well protected by reddish-brown skin. Yields up to 25% more than Longkeeping Yellow keeping in prime condition until March following. (Dob)
Dob; EWK; Rog

Sante Red
A heavy yield of virus free bulbs of very high quality. Plant this non-hybrid type in mid-April, sowing before this may result in bolting in a difficult season, harvesting during August. (Tuck)
Tuck

Topper
Big improvement on Giant Yellow. The plants are very vigorous, with stronger foliage and the crop is 30% bigger. Beautiful bright golden bulbs will store without rotting for an exceptionally long time, at least until May. Mild, refined onion flavour, excellent for cooking, salads or pickling. (Mars)
Mars

Yellow
Particularly fine, highly aromatic flavour. Many prefer these firm, small onions to the "ordinary" onions that have a somewhat sharper flavour. (Bakk)
Bakk; CGar; EWK

Yellow Long Keeping
Good large crops of high quality golden, yellow bulbs. Ideal for pickling as well as cooking and in salads. Stores extremely well. (Foth)
Foth

Skirret
Sium sisarum
The roots are cooked, like those of salsify and scorzonera. Could surely do with more selection to produce a fine vegetable.

Skirret
Native of China and certainly an ancient vegetable. The plant produces a "bundle" of swollen edible roots which are tender and sweet and floury. Use in the same way as salsify. (Suff)
CHAM; CHIL; FUTU; OGC; POYN; SUFF

Soya Bean
Glycine max
Fiskeby V Soy Bean
Very high protein bean and one of the most nutritionally valuable crops you can grow. Contains many of those nutritional elements lacking in other fruits and vegetables. Rich in phosphorus, iron, potassium, thiamine and calcium. Also rich in lecithin which helps to break up cholesterol and other fatty substances. Soybeans can be eaten cooked like other beans, toasted, ground into flour, and made into cheese or milk. The delicate flavour of soybeans will readily take up other flavourings. Requires long growing season and will grow in quite poor soils. Does not like excess nitrogen. (Suff)
SUFF

Gion Green Soy Bean
A vigorous variety maturing early, in 90 days from sowing. The large dark green pods are picked and cooked when still green. Either eat hot like French beans or allow to cool, shell out the seeds and eat as a snack. (OGC)
OGC; SMM; SUFF

Green Soy Bean
SMM

Soya
CHAM

Spinach
Spinacia oleracea and others
America
YATE

Atlanta
Highly versatile variety. Sow March to May for May to June cropping and mid July to early October for use from early September to late November. High yielding, frost resistant strain with thick dark green leaves. (EWK)
EWK; SBS

Atlanta
SBS

F1 Attica
BREE

Bazaroet
Ideal kitchen garden spinach, extremely prolific (exclusively female plants). Resistant to mildew. (Bakk)
BAKK

Bergola
An early maturing variety for use under glass. Sow at intervals from autumn to spring. Some resistance to Downy Mildew. (OGC)
OGC; SBS

Bloomsdale
Deep green leaves with high vitamin C content. Slow running to seed. (Mars)
CHIL; MARS; SBS; VANH

Broad Leaved Prickly
Winter variety that stands well, and produces deep green fleshy leaves. Very hardy. (OGC)
BAKK; BRWN; CGAR; CHIL; JOHN; JWB; OGC; SBS; SMM; VANH

Broad Leaved Prickly Standwell
SBS

F1 Carambole
BREE

F1 Correnta
RSLU

F1 Dash
SBS

Dominant
Thick, round, dark green leaves. Resistant to bolting. Heavy cropper. Round seeded, for spring or autumn sowing. (Toze)
JOHN; JWB; SBS; TOZE

Fabris
SBS

Spinach

F1 Galan
BAKK

Giant Thick Leaved see Broad Leaved Prickly
Giant Winter
Well-known, late autumn and winter spinach, very much in demand. Can withstand some frost. Strong variety, highly disease-resistant. (Bakk)
BAKK; TOZE

Grodane
Produces an abundance of fleshy leaves. Sow in spring, summer or autumn for an all year round supply. Good resistance to bolting. (Tuck)
TUCK

Hollandia
SBS

King of Denmark
SBS

Longstanding Round
Quick growing, with dark green leaves. (Sutt)
JOHN; T&M

F1 Mazurka
RSLU; SBS

Medania
This is a good variety for summer spinach which produces erect thick green smooth leaves. Vigorous, slow to bolt and resistant to mildew, it can be grown from spring through to late autumn. (OGC)
BRWN; JOHN; OGC; SBS; SUFF; TOZE; UNWI; YATE

F1 Melody
RSLU

Monarch Long Standing
A well-known and popular variety. (Unwi)
UNWI

Monnopa
Unique spinach, with low oxalic acid (an agent that causes loss of calcium from the blood). (T&M)
OGC; SBS; T&M

New Zealand
Different to usual spinach. Low growing shoots can be picked during summer and autumn. Not frost hardy. Thrives in dry sunny places. Germination can be difficult: soak seed before sowing in pots or outside under cloches March to May. (D&D)
> Bakk; CGar; Chil; D&D; Dob; EWK; Futu; John; JWB; OGC; Rog; SbS; Suff; Sutt; Wall

Nobel
> SbS

Noorman
> Bakk

Nores
Late-bolting summer spinach; a strongly improved variety which is highly resistant to mildew. Produces extremely high yields. Flavour outstanding. (Bakk)
> SbS

Norvak
Produces an abundance of fleshy leaves. Sow in spring, summer or autumn for an all year round supply. Good resistance to bolting. (Tuck)
> Dob; Mole; SbS

F1 Novadane
> Yate

F1 Oscar
> SbS

F1 Parys
> Toze

F1 Pavana
> RSlu

F1 Polka
> John; RSlu; SbS

F1 Predane
> Yate

Prickly New Giant
> Mole; SbS; Wall

Prickly Winter
Sow in autumn for spring cutting. Strong growing, producing heavy crops of large, dark green leaves. (EWK)
> D&D; EWK; Rog; Tuck

F1 Rhythm
> RSlu

Spinach

Round Summer
Good cropping summer spinach. (D&D)
CGar; D&D; EWK; Rog

Securo
Round-seeded, quick growing variety for spring and autumn cultivation. Resistant to mildew. One of the most cultivated spinach varieties. (Bakk)
Bakk

Sigmaleaf
Sutt

F1 Space
Foth; Mole

F1 Spartacus
SbS

Spinoza
SbS

F1 Splendour
Mole

F1 Sprint
SbS

F1 Sputnik
VanH

Strawberry
A reintroduced variety first grown and eaten over 400 years ago. It has smaller, thinner leaves than the modern spinach and at each leaf axil an abundance of small strawberry-like, thumb-nail sized fruits appear after flowering. The fruits are edible and the plant should be treated and used as any other spinach. (Foth)
Foth

F1 Symphony
Mars

F1 Triade
Cart; Foth

F1 Trias
Bree

F1 Triathlon
Mars

F1 Tribute
SbS

F1 Triton
SUTT

F1 Valeta
RSLU

Viking
A first class variety rich in vitamins, minerals, protein and with a superb taste. One of the best. (Foth)
FOTH; SBS

Virkade
Round-seeded for autumn sowing. Resistant to cucumber mosaic and is therefore most useful wherever this disease causes yellowing and stunting in overwintered crops of susceptible varieties. (Toze)
TOZE

Viroflay
For spring and autumn cultivation. Extremely suitable for wintering. Old, well-known variety which is still unbelievably popular. (Bakk)
BAKK; SBS

Viroflex
RSLU

Wobli
Dark green, slow bolting variety for summer and autumn use. (Toze)
MOLE; SBS; TOZE; WALL

F1 Wolter
BREE

Spinach Beet

Beta vulgaris
Also known as Chard and Seakale Beet; grown for the leaves and their fleshy midribs.

Erbette
Traditional cut and come again leaf beet from Italy. Grown for its fine tasting greens of good texture. (Suff)
SUFF

Fordhook Giant
Similar to Perpetual Spinach but has dark green leaves with a broad white rib. Provides greens throughout the summer and autumn. (OGC)
BRWN; CGAR; CHIL; D&D; EWK; MARS; OGC; ROG; SBS; SMM; TOZE; UNWI

Squash

Italian
White stemmed with dark green foliage. Sow March to August, and thin to eight inches. (Suff)
> SUFF

Lucullus
A much more prolific form, with an abundance of large, tasty leaves and wide, white mid-ribs. Cook the succulent mid-rib like asparagus and serve with melted butter. (T&M)
> BAKK; SBS; T&M

Lyon
Well-known variety. Excellent flavour. (Bakk)
> BAKK

Perpetual Spinach
Should be cooked and eaten like spinach. Can be harvested several times. (Bakk)
> BAKK; BREE; BRWN; CART; CGAR; CHIL; DOB; EWK; FOTH; JOHN; JWB; MARS; MOLE; OGC; SBS; SMM; SUTT; T&M; TOZE; TUCK; UNWI; VANH; WALL; YATE

Rhubarb Chard
Long stalks of bright crimson with dark green, deeply crumpled leaves. Highly decorative for floral arrangements as well as a valuable vegetable in the kitchen. Sow and grow as seakale. (Dob)
> BRWN; CGAR; CHIL; DOB; EWK; JOHN; JWB; OGC; ROG; SBS; SMM; SUFF; T&M; TUCK; WALL

Ruby Chard see Rhubarb Chard
Silver Chard see Seakale Beet
Swiss Chard see Fordhook Giant
> DOB; FOTH; JOHN; JWB; MOLE; SBS; TUCK; VANH; WALL

Swiss Chard see Fordhook Giant

Squash

Cucurbita spp.

The classification of squashes, pumpkins gourds, marrows, &c is fraught with difficulties. Essentially, summer squashes are good fresh and do not store long. Winter Squashes and pumpkins will store well, particularly if allowed to cure at a good temperature.

F1 All Seasons
> BREE

Chilacayote
A rampant, spreading vine that will trail for several yards or can be trained up fences and trellises. Produces enormous bright green and white mottled fruits, with white flesh containing black seeds. A native of South America, in Mexico it is used to make a dessert called Chilacayote. It is also eaten in France as a jam called Cheveux d'ange. Young fruits can be eaten like courgettes and when mature they can be stored for over a year. Tolerates cooler weather than other squashes, and is sometimes used as a disease-resistant rootstock for other Cucurbits. The seeds can be roasted and eaten, and are also grown for their high oil content. (Futu)

FUTU

F1 Gourmet Globe
T&M

F1 Sunburst
BREE; EWK; SUFF

Squash Pumpkin

Atlantic Giant
Holds the world record with a weight of 314 kg. Water and fertilize well. (Bakk)

BAKK; FOTH; JWB; MARS; SUTT; T&M; UNWI

Autumn Gold
These interesting round, lemon yellow fruits, often reaching 7-10 lb. are produced on semi-trailing plants. (Sutt)

SUTT

Big Max
Can grow very large under ideal conditions, large globe 17 in. X 17 in., orange pattern on pink background. Thick coarse skin, orange flesh. Long growing season. (Bree)

BREE

Big Moon
A novelty pumpkin with huge, late maturing fruit. The farm shop crowd puller. (Yate)

YATE

F1 Bushfire
SBS

Connecticut Field
Approx. 101 days to maturity. Weighs in at 15-25 lb. Large size and bright orange colour. (Suff)

SBS; SUFF

Squash Pumpkin

F1 Funny Face
SBS; YATE

Ghost Rider
Normally 12-20 lb. in weight. Deep orange colour. Fine quality with good strong handles. (Toze)
JOHN; TOZE

Halloween
Normally 6-10 lb. in weight. High yielding variety maturing early September. Fruits start life yellow in colour. (Toze)
BRWN; TOZE

Howden
Normally 15-25 lb. in weight. Deep orange, ribbed fruits. Good handles. (Toze)
TOZE

Hundredweight
A popular edible pumpkin. Will grow to a large size. (Tuck)
CGAR; D&D; EWK; ROG; SMM; SUTT; TUCK; VANH; WALL

Jack Be Little
The tiniest most decorative pumpkin. Bright orange and distinctly ribbed. They make charming table decorations. Eating quality is superb. Sweet and floury when baked. Perfect for stuffing. (Suff)
CGAR; EWK; OGC; SBS; SUFF

Jack O' Lantern
Deep globe with flattened ends, medium orange colour. Size 8 in., weight about 4-5 kg. Fine variety for Jack O' Lanterns. Medium maturity. (Bree)
BREE; CGAR; EWK; SBS

Jackpot
Compact, bush-type plants produce a heavy crop of 25 cm. (10 in.) diameter orange-yellow fruit which will store until Christmas. (Unwi)
UNWI

Jaune Gros de Paris
SBS

Large Yellow
SBS

Mammoth
A "biggy", producing yellow skinned and orange fleshed fruits. A favourite. (Foth)
BAKK; BRWN; CGAR; CHIL; DOB; FOTH; JOHN; JWB; MARS; MOLE; OGC; RSLU; SBS

Munchkin
MOLE; SBS; WALL

Peelless Pumpkin
Originally found in Styria, part of Austria, where it is still very popular, it has several culinary uses, the main one of which is the almost black seeds which can be eaten without peeling, hence peelless pumpkin, and which have a pleasant nut-like taste. A salad oil can be extracted from then and not least you can eat the pumpkin part as a pumpkin. The oil is said to be very effective for prostate problems and for strengtheningh the bladder. (Chil)
CHIL

Pumpkin
SBS

Small Sugar
A trailing variety, not especially vigorous. Medium fruits with bright orange flesh which store well. (OGC)
EWK; JOHN; OGC; SBS; TOZE; YATE

Spellbound
Normally 8-12 lb. in weight. Semi-bush type, early maturing. High yields of bright orange, smooth, round fruits. (Toze)
TOZE

F1 Spirit
MOLE; SBS; YATE

Sumo
Exhibition size pumpkin. Round in shape and bright orange in colour. (Toze)
TOZE

Triple Treat
Cucurbita moschata. Bright orange with delicate fine grain flesh and hull-less seeds (for sprouting, roasting or frying). Often grown for Halloween. Ideal for carving. (Suff)
SBS; SUFF

Uchiki Kuri
Japanese Pumpkin. Produces a heavy crop of bright orange, tear-drop shaped fruit with yellow flesh and a sweet and nutty flavour. (OGC)
CGAR; EWK; OGC; SBS; TUCK

Squash Summer
Cucurbita spp
F1 Patty Pan
BAKK

Squash Winter

F1 Scallopini
YATE

F1 Tivoli
DOB; MARS; MOLE; SBS; SUTT; T&M; UNWI; YATE

Squash Winter
Cucurbita spp.

Buttercup
Firm dense flesh with a superb sweet flavour. For soups, roasting round the joint and pumpkin pie and curd. Unusual shape and green/grey in colour. (Suff)
BRWN; OGC; SUFF; TOZE

Butternut
The cylindrical fruits have only a small seed cavity and the bright orange flesh is sweet, fine-grained and of excellent quality. (Dob)
CGAR; EWK; FOTH; MARS; SBS; TUCK; UNWI

F1 Cream of the Crop
T&M

Crown Prince
Steel blue in colour, bright orange flesh. Up to 10lb. in weight. Stores well. (Toze)
MARS; TOZE

F1 Delica
MOLE; SBS; TOZE; YATE

F1 Early Butternut
DOB; MOLE; YATE

Gem
Cricket ball sized, black/green fruits maturing from mid August. Very high yielding. (Toze)
FUTU; MARS; OGC; SUFF; TOZE

Gold Nugget
EWK; FUTU; OGC; SBS; TUCK; YATE

Golden Hubbard
Medium-size, oval fruits of excellent quality. Suitable for winter use. (Sutt)
JOHN; OGC; OGC; SBS; SUTT

F1 Goldkeeper
SBS; YATE

F1 Nutty Delica
BAKK

Onion
Brilliant orange/red coloured fruits of onion shape. 1-3 lb. in weight. (Toze)
Toze

Pompeon
Delicious Japanese winter squash; shiny almost black flat globe shape with golden flesh of superb eating quality as a sweet or savoury. (OGC)
OGC; Suff

Ponca
Butternut type. Cylindrical buff coloured fruits with very dense flesh and small seed cavity. Weight from 2 lb. (Toze)
Toze

Red Kuri
A very select and beautiful squash. Stunning bright orange tear drop shaped fruit weighing from 5-8 lb. Delicious smooth textured flesh. (Suff)
Suff

Rolet
A well flavoured South African gem squash type. An improvement on Little Gem both in yield and fruit size. Better for the small garden. Compact, high yielding vines producing lots of apple sized, black/green fruits which mature to bright orange. Excellent culinary qualities. (T&M)
T&M

Sweet Dumpling
Produces a large number of small fruits. Pale cream striped skin with creamy white flesh. Ideal for stuffing with meat and baking whole. (EWK)
Brwn; CGar; Chil; EWK; SbS; Suff; T&M; Toze; Tuck

Sweet Mama
Bushy butter type producing masses of dark green flattish fruits. Very sweet, bright yellow flesh with dry nutty flavour. (EWK)
Brwn; CGar; EWK; SbS

F1 Table Ace
Brwn; Foth; Mole; Toze; Yate

Turk's Turban
Brightly coloured and usually grown for ornamental purposes, these are also very tasty if picked young. Trailing variety. (OGC)
CGar; EWK; OGC; SbS; Suff; Tuck

Swede

Brassica napus var. napobrassica
Yet another member of the cabbage family, grown for its enlarged root.

Acme
Popular fast growing variety with large fine textured roots. (D&D)
MAS; MOLE; RSLU; SBS; WALL

Acme Garden Purple Top
Popular fast growing variety with large fine textured roots. (D&D)
CGAR; CHIL; D&D; EWK; JOHN; OGC; ROG; SMM

Angela
Produces purple, globe shaped roots of uniform shape and size. Good resistance to powdery mildew. Suitable for early harvest. (Bree)
BREE; JOHN; RSLU; YATE

Best Of All
Yellow-fleshed globe with purple skin. Very hardy, will stand all winter. (Mars)
BRWN; CGAR; D&D; EWK; FOTH; MARS; MOLE; ROG; SBS; SMM; T&M; UNWI; VANH; WALL

Blauwkop
Extremely heavy cropper with excellent keeping qualities. (VanH)
VANH

Champion Purple Top
SBS

Devon Champion
One of the most popular varieties outstanding for table use. (Tuck)
TUCK

Doon Major
JOHN

Laurentian
Dark purple, globe shaped roots, with very little neck and compact foliage. Ideal type for market swedes. (Bree)
BREE; JOHN; RSLU; SBS; YATE

Lizzy
Bred specially for improved flavour, has a lovely sweet taste. Attractive internal and external coloration with excellent tolerance against root cracking and bolting. (Dob)
BRWN; CART; DOB; FOTH; JOHN

Magnificent
CART; MAS

Magres
A selection in Ruta Otofte with very high dry matter and very good resistance to powdery mildew. (Bree)
BREE; JOHN; SBS; TOZE; YATE

Marian
A very high yielding variety of good flavour and texture, resistant to club root and mildew. (D&D)
BREE; BRWN; CGAR; D&D; DOB; EWK; FOTH; JOHN; JWB; MARS; MAS; MOLE; OGC; ROG; RSLU; SBS; SUFF; TOZE; TUCK; UNWI; VANH; WALL; YATE

Peerless
MAS; SBS

Ruta Otofte
Purple skinned, round to slightly tankard shaped, with high dry matter and good winter hardiness. (Bree)
BREE; JOHN; SBS; SMM

Western Perfection
Quick-growing, almost neckless, purple-topped roots with yellow flesh. Ready to lift as required from September. (Sutt)
SUTT

Wilhemsburger Gelbe
(Formerly Pandur) A very early and cold-hardy fibreless variety with attractive pink top. (T&M)
MAS; T&M

Sweetcorn

Zea mays
Should be planted in a block, not rows, to ensure good pollination.

F1 Aztec
JOHN

F1 Butterscotch
T&M

F1 Candle
RSLU; SUTT

F1 Challenger
SBS; TOZE

F1 Champ
MARS; SBS; T&M

Sweetcorn

F1 Citation
Toze

F1 Classic
SbS

F1 Cobham Sweet
Toze

F1 Comanche
John

F1 Concorde
RSlu

F1 Conquest
Dob; Mole; T&M; Toze; Wall

F1 Dawn
CGar; OGC; Rog; SbS; Suff; Tuck

F1 Dickson
Bree

F1 Dynasty
Bree; Toze

F1 Earlibelle
SbS; Sutt; Toze

F1 Earliking
Brwn; Chil; John; Mole; OGC; SbS; Toze

F1 Earlivee
Toze

F1 Early Cup
SbS

F1 Early Pac
EWK; SbS; Toze

F1 Early Xtra Sweet
SbS; Unwi

F1 Excel
Bree

F1 Fiesta
Foth; Mole; SbS

F1 First Of All
Sutt

F1 Florida Stay Sweet
SBS

Golden Bantam
JOHN; MOLE; SBS

F1 Golden Sweet
EWK; OGC; SBS; YATE

F1 Herald
MOLE; WALL

F1 Honey and Cream
MARS

F1 Honeycomb
SBS; SMM; SUFF; TUCK

F1 Honeydew
FOTH; JWB; SBS

F1 Honeysweet
YATE

F1 Indian Dawn
TOZE

John Innes Hybrid
JOHN; MAS

John Innes Hybrid Canada Cross
SBS

F1 Jubilee
BREE; BRWN; EWK; JOHN; MOLE; SBS; TOZE; YATE

Kelvedon Glory
Crops well, early and yields high quality, long, even cobs of exceptional flavour.
(Foth)
D&D; EWK; FOTH; JOHN; MAS; MOLE; OGC; ROG; SBS; UNWI; WALL

F1 Kelvedon Sweetheart
SBS

F1 Kodiak
SBS

F1 Lariat
TOZE

F1 Lumidor
RSLU

Sweetcorn

F1 Mellogold
JOHN

F1 Minisweet
OGC

F1 Minor
FOTH; JOHN

F1 Miracle
EWK; ROG; SBS; VANH; WALL

F1 Morning Sun
D&D; OGC; ROG; SBS; SUFF; VANH; WALL

F1 Northern Belle
EWK; JOHN; MOLE; SBS; TOZE

F1 Northern Extra Sweet
SBS; TOZE

F1 Northern Star
SBS

F1 October Gold
JOHN; SBS

F1 Ovation
TOZE

F1 Peppy
BAKK

F1 Pilot
BREE

F1 Pinnacle
T&M; TOZE

F1 Reward
BRWN; JOHN; MARS

F1 Rosella 425
EWK; SBS

F1 Royal Crest
SBS

F1 Seneca Horizon
TOZE

F1 Seneca Star
TOZE

F1 Showcase
BREE

F1 Snogold
SBS; YATE

F1 Snosweet
YATE

F1 Starlite
EWK; OGC; SBS

F1 Sugar Boy
CGAR; EWK; OGC; ROG; SBS; SMM

F1 Sugar King
SBS

Summer Flavour
Very early maturing which makes it ideal for Northern districts, poor summers and late sowings. Plus gourmet sweet, very tender and tasty 6.5-7 in. cobs. (T&M)
T&M

F1 Sundance
BRWN; DOB; JWB; SBS; SUTT; TOZE; UNWI

F1 Sunrise
CART; DOB; MARS; SBS; TOZE

F1 Sweet 77
BRWN; CGAR; D&D; JOHN; JWB; MOLE; ROG; SBS; SMM; SUFF; TOZE; VANH; WALL

F1 Sweet Bonus
EWK; SBS

F1 Sweet Nugget
SBS

F1 Sweet Season
OGC

F1 Sweet September
TOZE

F1 Tasty Sweet
BAKK; EWK; SBS

F1 Terrific
SBS

F1 Trophy
RSLU

Teff

F1 Two's Sweeter
T&M

F1 Xtra Sweet Improved
Mars

F1 Yukon
SBS; SMM

Teff
Agrostis tef
A staple in Ethiopia, it may have something to offer gardeners in the U.K.

Teff
Futu

Texsel Greens
Brassica carinata
Mild flavoured, large-leaved summer greens which can be eaten as salad, steamed or stir fried. Said to resist pests and diseases better than many other varieties of Brassica.

Ethiopian Rape see Texsel Greens
Texsel Greens
This leafy vegetable is milder in flavour than cabbage and much more tasty than spinach. Ideal to pick and eat fresh, but will also keep in cold storage. Can be frozen. (Brwn)
Brwn; Futu; Suff; Yate

Tiger Nut
Cyperus esculentus
A sedge with narrow, dark green leaves, producing large numbers of small brown tubers. These tubers have a sweet, nutty flavour and can be eaten raw, ground with water to make a drink, or roasted to make a coffee substitute.

Tiger Nuts
Futu

Tomatillo
Physalis ixocarpa
A Mexican annual with tomato-like fruits, closely related to the Chinese Lantern and Cape Gooseberry. Fruits can be up to 6 cm. across and are enclosed in a papery husk that splits to reveal the ripe fruit. They prefer a rich, light soil and should be grown like out-

door tomatoes. Tomatillos ripen sooner and in cooler weather than tomatoes, and are not susceptible to potato blight, a real problem for outdoor tomatoes in a wet season. Best used cooked in place of tomatoes in sauces and the like, and will keep in storage for many weeks.

Large Green
Large green fruits. (Futu)
FUTU

Purple
Smaller fruit with a sharper flavour and purple colour, preferred by some Mexican cooks. (Futu)
FUTU

Tomato
Lycopersicon lycopersicum
F1 1317
YATE

F1 936
YATE

F1 Abunda
CGAR; JOHN; MOLE; SBS

Ailsa Craig
Greenhouse/outdoor, cordon. Medium size fruit, very regular and perfect in shape. For real flavour, this is still one of the very best and it's a heavy cropper. (Unwi)
BREE; BRWN; CGAR; CHIL; D&D; DOB; EWK; FOTH; JOHN; JWB; MARS; MOLE; OGC; ROG; SBS; SMM; SUTT; TOZE; UNWI; VANH; WALL; YATE

F1 Alfresco
BRWN; JOHN; JWB; SBS; TOZE

Alicante
Outdoor/greenhouse, cordon. An ideal variety for beginners, producing a heavy crop of high quality well flavoured fruit. (T&M)
BREE; BRWN; CART; CGAR; D&D; DOB; EWK; FOTH; JOHN; JWB; MARS; MOLE; OGC; ROG; SBS; SUTT; T&M; TOZE; TUCK; UNWI; VANH; WALL; YATE

F1 Allegro
YATE

F1 Angela
CGAR; JOHN; JWB; MOLE; SBS

F1 Arasta
BRWN; CGAR; EWK; JOHN; MOLE; ROG; SBS; TUCK; WALL

Tomato

F1 Atlantic City
EWK; SBS

Aurega
Dwarf variety for outdoors, fruit medium to small. (CGar)
EWK; SUFF

F1 Beefmaster
BAKK; CGAR; EWK; ROG; SBS; SMM; VANH; WALL

F1 Big Boy
Greenhouse/outdoors, cordon. Fairly large, very fleshy fruits with few seeds. (Sutt)
CGAR; DOB; EWK; FOTH; JOHN; JWB; MARS; MOLE; OGC; ROG; SBS; SUFF; TUCK; UNWI; WALL; YATE

F1 Blizzard
CGAR; FOTH; MOLE; SBS; TOZE; WALL; YATE

Britains Breakfast
Lemon shaped fruit, red and very sweet, standard habit, has a very large spreading truss with many having over 60 fruits. Fruit does not split when ripe. (Rob)
CGAR; ROB

F1 Buffalo
BAKK; JOHN

F1 Calypso
MOLE; SBS; TOZE

F1 Carmello
BREE

F1 Cherry Belle
CART; DOB; SUTT; YATE

F1 Cherry Wonder
CGAR; DOB; FOTH; YATE

F1 Choice
BREE

F1 Contessa
BAKK

F1 Cossack
CGAR

F1 Counter
CGAR; TOZE; UNWI

Craigella
Non greenback similar to Ailsa Craig. (CGar)
CGAR; EWK; SBS

F1 Cumulus
DOB

F1 Curabel
JWB; SBS

F1 Curato
CGAR

F1 Cyclon
BRWN; CGAR; UNWI; YATE

F1 Danny
CGAR; JOHN; JWB; MOLE; SBS

F1 Dombello
DOB; JOHN; MOLE; SBS; YATE

F1 Dombito
BRWN; JWB; MARS; T&M; TOZE; YATE

Earliana
SBS

F1 Else
CGAR

F1 Estrella
BAKK; BRWN; DOB; SBS

F1 Eurocross BB
CGAR; EWK; JOHN; JWB; MOLE; ROG; SBS; WALL; YATE

F1 Extase
CGAR; EWK; ROG; SBS

First In The Field
Very good for outdoor culture, vigorous growth. (CGar)
CGAR; EWK; JOHN; JWB; MOLE; SBS; WALL

F1 French Cross
SUTT

Freude see Gardener's Delight

Gardener's Delight

Small cherry-type fruit of outstanding flavour, ideal for salads and sandwiches, which can also be frozen complete. An exceptional cropper both outdoors and under glass. (OGC)

> BREE; BRWN; CART; CGAR; CHIL; D&D; DOB; EWK; FOTH; JOHN; JWB; MARS; MOLE; OGC; ROG; SBS; SUFF; SUTT; T&M; TOZE; TUCK; UNWI; WALL; YATE

F1 Gemini

> DOB

Golden Sunrise

For those who like a little variation in their tomatoes. As the name indicates this is golden yellow in colour, medium in size, round, thin skinned, excellent flavour and a heavy cropper. Early. (OGC)

> BRWN; CGAR; CHIL; D&D; DOB; EWK; FOTH; JOHN; JWB; MOLE; OGC; ROG; SBS; SUFF; SUTT; T&M; TUCK; WALL

F1 Golden boy

> SUTT

F1 Goldstar

> CGAR; MOLE; SBS

F1 Grenadier

> CGAR; ROG; SBS; SUTT; WALL

Harbinger

An old favourite from the beginning of the century when tomatoes had flavour! A good tall outdoor variety or for growing under plastic. Thin skinned medium size fruit which will ripen well off the plant. (Suff)

> CGAR; DOB; EWK; JWB; OGC; SBS; SUFF; SUTT; TOZE

Heinz

> SBS

Histon Early

Outdoor, cordon. A heavy cropper with bright red fruit of good size and quality and fine flavour. (Unwi)

> UNWI

F1 Holland Brid

> CGAR

F1 Husky Gold

> T&M

Jubilee

> ROB

Tomato

Kondine Red
Deep scarlet fruit on large trusses, heavy cropper. (CGar)
CGAR

F1 Liberto
CGAR

F1 Libra
BRWN

F1 MM
CGAR

Magnum
Dutch early variety, non greenback, cladosporium resistance, A. B. resistance. (CGar)
T&M

Maja
Bush type of compact growing habit with very good tolerance to cool conditions. Bright red fruits up to 35cms each plant with strong aromatic flavour. (EWK)
EWK

F1 Manhattan
BREE

Marglobe
Large red fruit, thick meaty flesh of excellent flavour can be grown to over 1 lb each tomato. (Rob)
CGAR; ROB; SBS

Marmande VR
Outdoor, cordon. Large, firm irregular fruits of the Continental type, with very few seeds. Ideal for slicing. A semi-determinate type producing terminal trusses. Early. (Unwi)
CHIL; EWK

Marmande hative see Marmande Super
Marmande super
A variety originating in Southern Europe, producing large, irregular shaped, fleshy tomatoes ideal for slicing and of a rich flavour. Shows good natural resistance to disease, and best results are obtained when grown outdoors. Bushy habit. (OGC)
BAKK; CGAR; DOB; FOTH; JOHN; JWB; MARS; MOLE; OGC; ROG; SBS; SUFF; SUTT; T&M; UNWI; WALL

F1 Master
BAKK

Tomato

F1 Matador
CGAR; T&M; YATE

Minibel
Tasty bite-size tomatoes can be grown in pots on the patio, in window boxes or on your windowsill, novel, miniature bush variety. (Foth)
FOTH; MARS

F1 Mirabell
FOTH; MARS

Moneycross
Greenhouse, cordon. An improvement on the popular Moneymaker variety being a heavy cropper of non greenback fruit. (John)
CGAR; JOHN; JWB; MOLE; SBS; VANH

Moneymaker
Outdoor/greenhouse, cordon. Very reliable variety which has stood the test of time. (T&M)
BREE; BRWN; CART; CGAR; CHIL; DOB; EWK; FOTH; JOHN; MOLE; ROG; SBS; SMM; SUTT; T&M; TOZE; TUCK; UNWI; VANH; WALL; YATE

Moneymaker Dutch Victory
TOZE

Moneymaker Stonor
A very heavy cropper, with fruits of medium size, bright scarlet in colour. (Barb)
CGAR; JWB

Montfavet 63-4
A so-called bush type tomato, early maturing and fleshy, with a beautiful round shape. Resistant to "bursting" and, therefore, a sure cropper. Very suitable for early cultivation under glass. Perfectly suited for making tomato juice and ketchup. (Bakk)
BAKK

F1 Monza
CGAR; EWK

F1 Nimbus
SUTT

F1 Ostona
YATE

Outdoor Girl
This variety has been developed for outdoor cultivation, and its characteristics include extreme earliness, large trusses bearing many medium sized fruit, excellent flavour, a good red colour and sturdy plants. An ideal outdoor garden variety. (John)
CGAR; D&D; EWK; JOHN; JWB; MARS; MOLE; OGC; ROG; SBS; WALL

Oxheart
The traditional Italian garden tomato. Huge pink fruit shaped like a heart. Flesh is very meaty with not too much juice so ideal for slicing, sandwiches, &c. Produced an excellent crop under a polytunnel. (Suff)
SBS; SUFF

F1 Pannovy
BREE

F1 Patio
BAKK

F1 Phyra
CGAR; EWK; FOTH; OGC; SBS; SUFF

F1 Pipo
Greenhouse/outdoor. Dwarf non greenback, mid season tomato. (CGar)
CGAR

F1 Piranto
MARS

F1 Pixie
CGAR; D&D; EWK; JOHN; JWB; MOLE; OGC; ROG; SBS; SMM; SUFF; WALL

Plumito
Smooth straight sided red fruit, sweet and fleshy, ideal for freezer or bottling, standard habit. (Rob)
ROB

Plumpton King
Popular red English greenback variety, unsurpassable for quality. (CGar)
CGAR

F1 Prelude
YATE

F1 Primato
BREE; DOB; WALL

F1 Prisca
MARS

Red Alert
Outdoor/greenhouse, bush. Small fruits roughly 1 oz each with a good flavour. Easy. No side shooting or training. (T&M)
BAKK; BRWN; CART; CGAR; D&D; DOB; EWK; FOTH; JOHN; JWB; MARS; MOLE; OGC; ROG; SBS; SUFF; UNWI; WALL

Tomato

Red Cherry
Cherry sized fruit, good flavour, standard habit with long strings of fruit. (Rob)
 Rob

Roma VF
Outdoor, bush. Continental type bearing brightly coloured long, fleshy fruits. Heavy cropping, and resistant to fusarium wilt. (Sutt)
 CGar; Foth; Mars; SbS; T&M

Round Yellow Sunrise
Notably sweeter in flavour than most red tomatoes, standard habit. (Rob)
 Rob

Rutgers
 SbS

San Marzano
 D&D

San Marzano 2
A typical "Italian" tomato, producing longish, firm fruit. Extremely suitable for making the sauce that goes with spaghetti Bolognese, for tomato soup or for garnishing your salads. It gives a high yield of egg-shaped, firm-fleshed fruit. (Bakk)
 Bakk; CGar; Chil; EWK; JWB; OGC; Rog; SbS; SMM; Suff; VanH; Wall

F1 Shirley
 Brwn; Cart; CGar; D&D; EWK; Foth; John; JWB; Mars; Mole; OGC; Rog; SbS; Sutt; T&M; Toze; Tuck; Unwi; VanH; Wall; Yate

F1 Sigmabush
 Sutt

F1 Sioux
 Unwi

F1 Sleaford Abundance
 CGar; JWB; Mars; SbS; Suff

F1 Sonatine
 JWB; Sutt

F1 Spartan
 Dob

F1 Spectra
 CGar; Mole

St Pierre
A very tasty traditional French tomato. Produces a late crop of large tasty bright red fruit, superb sliced for salad and sprinkled with fresh basil. (Suff)
 Suff

Stonor Exhibition
Medium early, round red fruit excellent for the show bench, has the good old fashioned taste. (Rob)
>JWB; Rob; Wall

Sub Arctic Plenty
>CGar

F1 Sungold
>T&M

F1 Super Cross
>SbS

F1 Supersteak
>T&M

F1 Sweet 100
>Bakk; Bree; Brwn; CGar; EWK; Foth; John; Mars; Mole; OGC; SbS; SMM; Suff; Sutt; T&M

Sweet Chelsea
>CGar

F1 Sweet Cherry
>Foth; SbS

F1 Sweet Susan
>CGar

The Amateur
Outdoor. A very popular bush tomato. Good yield and quality. (Unwi)
>Cart; CGar; Chil; D&D; EWK; Foth; John; JWB; Mole; OGC; Rog; SbS; Sutt; Unwi; VanH; Wall

Tigerella
>CGar; EWK; Foth; OGC; Rog; SbS; Suff; Sutt; T&M; Wall

Tiny Tim
The ultimate in compact tomato plants. Perfect for pot or window box growing. Superb flavoured cherry sized fruit which are quite delicious whole in salads. (Suff)
>CGar; EWK; Rog; SbS; Suff; Sutt; Tuck; VanH; Wall

F1 Tomboy
>CGar; D&D; EWK; SbS; Suff

F1 Tomboy Golden
>CGar; EWK; OGC; SbS

F1 Tornado
>Foth; Mars; Mole; SbS; Sutt; Wall

F1 Totem
CGAR; DOB; EWK; JOHN; MOLE; ROG; SBS; SMM; TUCK; UNWI

F1 Tumbler
BRWN; CART; CGAR; DOB; JOHN; MOLE; SBS; SUTT; T&M; UNWI; WALL; YATE

F1 Turbo
CGAR; JOHN; MOLE; SBS; TOZE; WALL

F1 Typhoon
BRWN; DOB; MOLE; SBS; WALL

F1 Virossa
SBS

Yellow Canary
MOLE; SBS; WALL

Yellow Cocktail
Delightful miniature, pear-shaped, golden-yellow fruits. Best grown under glass, tall sturdy plants quick growing with large trusses. (EWK)
EWK

Yellow Currant
Small fruit, grape-like in appearance, long strings of tomatoes. Can be grown as a standard type in a pot or as a bush habit. (Rob)
CGAR; ROB

Yellow Pearshaped
Pear shape fruit, very sweet and solid with few seeds, standard habit. (Rob)
BAKK; CGAR; ROB

Yellow Perfection
The earliest and most prolific tall yellow tomato in existence. Recommended for outdoors. Cordon. (Unwi)
MARS; UNWI

F1 Zorro
CGAR; EWK; SBS

Tree Tomato

Cyphomandra betacea

Tree Tomato
A first-rate attraction for indoors. Sow early, prick seedlings out into pots and put in a frost-free place during the winter. This decorative tree will bear fruit from the second year onwards. A real treat, raw as well as cooked. (Bakk)
BAKK

Tuberous Pea

Lathyrus sativus

An attractive trailing perennial, naturalised in some parts of Britain, with pink sweet-pea flowers. It produces small tubers on its roots for which it was once cultivated in Europe. The tubers have a pleasant flavour like a sweet chestnut and are eaten baked or boiled.

Tuberous Pea
FUTU

Turnip

Brassica rapa var. rapa

Aberdeen Green Top Yellow
SBS

Arcoat
SBS; YATE

Champion Green Top Yellow
One of the most popular yellow fleshed turnips grown. Remains firm and palatable over a long period. (Tuck)
TUCK

De Norfolk a collet vert see Imperial Green Globe
Early Snowball
Harvest when small, sweet and tender. Cook lightly and add a dab of butter. The variety grows quickly from a spring sowing. (Suff)
FOTH; SUFF

Early White see Snowball
Early White Stone
JOHN

Frisia
MAS

Goldana
BAKK

Golden Ball
Sow for succession from late spring onwards. Harvest when about tennis-ball size. Can be sown late August for winter storing in sand or peat. Good flavour. (D&D)
BRWN; CART; CGAR; D&D; DOB; EWK; FOTH; JOHN; JWB; MARS; MOLE; OGC; SBS; SUTT; TUCK; UNWI; VANH; WALL

Goudbal see Golden Ball
Green Globe see Imperial Green Globe

Green Top
SBS

Green Top Stone see Manchester Market

F1 Hakutaka
DOB

Imperial Green Globe
Maincrop with round roots of pure white flesh. The best variety to grow for turnip top "greens". (Sutt)
SUTT

Manchester Market
Large white globe, green top. (Mars)
BREE; BRWN; CGAR; D&D; EWK; JOHN; JWB; MARS; MOLE; RSLU; TOZE; WALL; YATE

F1 Market Express
YATE

Milan Early White Top
Very early, forces well under frame or cloche. (JWB)
JWB

Milan Purple Top Forcing
A very early garden turnip for sowing in the open, although it can also be sown in a frame. Sweet flavour, very rich in vitamins. (Bakk)
BAKK; BREE; RSLU; TOZE; WALL

Milan White
Flat shaped roots of pure white for early crops. (Dob)
BREE; DOB; EWK; JOHN; SBS; SMM; TOZE; VANH; WALL

Milan White Top see Milan White
Model White see Stone
Norfolk Green Globe see Imperial Green Globe
Orange Jelly see Golden Ball

Presto
Aptly named, this is a very small comma, pure white turnip that can be picked in little more than a month after sowing when the roots will be about one inch in diameter. Sow in rows and thin out to three inches apart. The leaves can also be eaten, cooked as for greens. (Chil)
CHIL

Purple Top Milan
Quick to mature and good for early sowings. It has distinctive white flat roots topped with purple which have an excellent flavour. (Foth)
> Brwn; Cart; CGar; Dob; EWK; Foth; John; Mole; SbS; SMM; Sutt; Tuck; Unwi

Purple Top White Globe
White globe shaped root with purple top. (Bree)
> Bakk; Bree; EWK; John; SbS; VanH

Red Milan
> SbS

F1 Royal Crown
> Suff

Snowball
Very fast growing. Tender flesh suitable for salads if harvested when young. (D&D)
> Brwn; Cart; CGar; Chil; D&D; EWK; John; JWB; Mars; MAS; Mole; OGC; SbS; SMM; Sutt; T&M; Tuck; Unwi; VanH; Wall; Yate

Sprinter see Milan Purple Top Forcing
Stanis
Round roots with deep pink shoulder. For late summer and autumn crops. (Toze)
> Toze

Stone
> Dob; Toze

Stubble Turnip see Typhon
F1 Tokyo Cross
> Bree; CGar; Dob; EWK; Foth; John; OGC; SbS; Suff; T&M; Yate

Tokyo Market Sagami see Presto
F1 Tokyo Top
> John

Tyfon
Cook the tops like spinach, very nutritious for humans and goats. (JWB)
> Bree; JWB; MAS

Veitch's Red Globe
Smooth skinned roots with red top and pure white flesh. Fast maturer. (OGC)
> John; OGC

Watermelon

Veitch's Red Globe see Purple Top White Globe

Water Chinquapin
Nelumbo lutea
A beautiful ornamental lotus from the US, growing in shallow water. It produces round leaves that are held above the water and huge pale yellow waterlily-like flowers. These are followed by unusual flat pepper-pot seedheads. The large seeds are delicious cooked like chestnuts. The young leaves were cooked like spinach by native tribes and the tubers were leached to remove bitterness and eaten, with a flavour likened to a sweet potato.

Water Chinquapin
FUTU

Watercress
Nasturtium officinalis
Imperial Large Leaved
SBS

Watercress
Running water is not essential for this variety which will grow in any moist place or in well watered pots. (OGC)
CGAR; CHAM; CHIL; DOB; EWK; JOHN; JWB; MOLE; OGC; ROG; SBS; SMM; SUFF; WALL

Watermelon
Citrullus lanatus
Charleston Gray
Fine eating variety with crisp red flesh and light greenish skin. Semi-long fruits which can grow to a large size. Needs a lot of watering. (EWK)
CGAR; EWK; JOHN; JWB; MOLE; OGC; SBS; SMM; WALL

Crimson Sweet
Produces large green-skinned fruit with a distinctive mouth watering aroma and very refreshing, juicy, scarlet flesh. (John)
JOHN

F1 Golden Crown
T&M

F1 Lucky Sweet
A hybrid which replaces the older type of water-melon because it has the merit of good fruit setting, even in low temperatures. (Bakk)
BAKK

Sugar Baby
Round fruits weighing up to 10 lbs. Sweet and juicy. Start seed early to get best results. 80 days. (Suff)
CHIL; FOTH; SBS; SUFF

Wild Rice
Zizania aquatica
An annual grain crop from North America, which grows in ponds, lakes and slow-moving rivers. A highly prized speciality food in its native area, it was traditionally harvested by bending the ripe heads over and knocking the seeds into a canoe. The seeds are then hulled and parched prior to cooking. Wild rice needs shallow water 15 — 45 cm. deep and a silty substrate in which to grow. It also needs a gentle through-flow of water to do well; a spring-fed pond would be an ideal site. Should reseed if conditions suit it.

Wild Rice
FUTU

Yacon
Polymnia sonchifolia
A frost-tender species from the Andes, which produces large storage tubers that look like dahlia roots, as well as vegetative tubers similar in appearance to Jerusalem artichokes. The plant is ornamental, producing large triangular leaves on thick stems, and reaches a height of 1.5 — 2 m. under ideal conditions. It makes a good accent plant for edible landscapes. The storage tubers have no buds, so they do not sprout and can be stored for long periods in a frost-free place. Plants have produced storage tubers weighing 1 Kg. with a crunchy texture and sweet flavour. Traditionally they are left in the sun for a few days after harvesting before being eaten. They retain their crunchiness after cooking and are an ideal substitute for water chestnuts in Chinese cookery.

Yacon
FUTU

Suppliers 1994

This year sees the loss of a few suppliers and the addition of a few others. Most of the new suppliers are specialists who, although their lists are small, are nevertheless providing access to otherwise scarce vegetables. We are always happy to add new suppliers to The Vegetable Finder so if you know of a mail-order source of vegetable seeds or plants that isn't already here, or if you are such a supplier, please let us know.

BAKK
Bakker Holland
P.O. Box 111
Spalding
Lincs
PE12 6EL
Phone: 0775 711411
Fax:
Latest catalogue we have is from 1992.

BENN
Michael Bennett
Long Compton
Shipston on Stour
Warwickshire
CV36 5JN
Phone:
Fax:
New this year. A supplier of asparagus crowns and artichoke offsets.

BIR
Jennifer Birch
Garfield Villa
Belle Vue Road
Stroud
GLOS
Phone: 0453 750371
Fax:
New this year. A specialist supplier of garlic.

BREE
Breeders Seeds Ltd
17 Summerwood Lane
Halsall
Ormskirk
Lancs
L39 8RQ
Phone: 0704 840775
Fax: 0704 841099
Specialises in bulk supplies, but some small packets also available. Latest catalogue we have is from 1993.

BRWN
D. T. Brown & Co Ltd
Station Road
Poulton Le Fylde
Blackpool
Lancs
FY6 7HX
Phone: 0253 882371
Fax: 0253 890923
A good range of small packets, but also supplies in greater bulk.

F1 Many	F1 Unique	OP Many	OP Unique

Suppliers

CGAR
Country Gardens
69/71 Main Street
East Leake
Leics
LE12 6PF
Phone: 0509 852905
Fax:
Latest catalogue we have is from 1992.

CALL
John Callum
Unit 51
Bandeath Industrial Estat
Throsk
by Stirling
FK7 7NP
Phone: 0786 815357
Fax: 0786 815357
Potato specialist, new to The Vegetable
Finder this year. Supplies large and small
quantities.

CART
Carters Tested Seeds Ltd
Hele Road
Torquay
Devon TQ2 7QJ
Phone: 0803 616156
Fax: 0803 615747

CHAM
John Chambers
15 Westleigh Road
Barton Seagrave
Kettering
Northants
NN15 5AJ
Phone: 0933 652562
Fax: 0933 652576
Famous for wild flowers, but also supply
many edible "weeds" and other unusual
pot-herbs and vegetables. Latest catalogue
we have is from 1992.

CHIL
Chiltern Seeds
Bortree Stile
Ulverston
Cumbria
LA12 7PB
Phone: 0229 581137
Fax: 0229 584549
An astonishing range of seeds, apart from
vegetables. Latest catalogue we have is
from 1993, as the new catalogue is always
one of the last to appear.

D&D
Dig and Delve Organics
Fen Road
Blo' Norton
Diss
Norfolk
IP22 2JH
Phone: 0379 898377
Fax:

DOB

Samuel Dobie & Son Ltd
Broomhill Way
Torquay
Devon
TQ2 7QW
Phone: 0803 616888
Fax:

EWK

E.W.King & Co. Ltd
Monks Farm
Pantlings Lane
Coggeshall Road
Kelvedon
CO5 9PG
Phone: 0376 570000
Fax:

Bulk supplies and smaller packets. A major wholesaler for other seed suppliers.

FOTH

Mr Fothergill's Seeds Ltd
Gazeley Road
Kentford
Newmarket
Suffolk
CB8 7QB
Phone: 0638 751161
Fax: 0638 751624

FUTU

Future Foods
3 Tai Madog
Stablau
Llanrug
Gwynedd
LL5 3PH
Phone: 0286 870606
Fax:

A truly wonderful catalogue, full of unusual edible plants. We have listed only the vegetables; Future Foods also supply trees and shrubs, unusual fruits, mushroom spawns, and starter cultures for fermented foods. Good selection of books, too.

HEN

James Henderson & Sons
Kingholm Quay
Dumfries
DG1 4SU
Phone: 0387 52234
Fax: 0387 62302

A potato specialist.

JWB

J.W. Boyce Seedsmen
Bush Pasture
Lower Carter Street
Fordham, Ely
Cambs
CB7 5JU
Phone: 0638 721158
Fax:

F1 Many	F1 Unique	OP Many	OP Unique

Suppliers

JOHN

W.W. Johnson and Son Ltd
London Road
Boston
Lincs
PE21 8AD
Phone: 0205 365051
Fax: 0205 310148

Supplies small packets and in bulk. Latest catalogue we have is from 1993.

MAS

M.A.S.
9 Brevel Terrace
Charlton Kings
Cheltenham
GL53 8JZ
Phone: 0242 234355
Fax:

Bulk only. Specialist in grass mixtures for all purposes. Also wildflowers and conservation mixtures.

MARS

S.E. Marshall & Co Ltd
Wisbech
Cambs
PE13 2RF
Phone: 0945 583407
Fax:

MART

J.E. Martin
4 Church Street
Market Harborough
Leics
LE16 7AA
Phone: 0858 462751
Fax: 0858 434544

Potato specialist.

McL

Mrs M. MacLean
Dornock Farm
Crieff
Perthshire
PH7 3QN
Phone: 0764 2472
Fax:

Wonderful range of potatoes, but rather limited availability. Please send SAE when enquiring. Two information leaflets available: Fact Sheet on Special Properties of Potato Varieties (revised 1990, price 50p) and Growing Potatoes for Exhibition (1987, price 30p).

MOLE

J. W. Moles & Son
Turkey Cock Lane
Stanway
Colchester
Essex
CO3 5PD
Phone: 0206 213213
Fax: 0206 212876

Bulk only. Moles will not deal in small quantities, and agreed to be included in this year's edition only if we pointed out that they will not reply to enquiries from amateurs.

OGC

Chase Organics (GB) Ltd
Coombelands House
Coombelands Lane
Addlestone
Weybridge
KT15 1HY
Phone: 0932 820958
Fax: 0932 821258

The HDRA's mail-order catalogue, with many sundries for organic gardening in addition to seeds.

PASK

A.R. Paske
The South Lodge
Gazeley Road
Kentford
Newmarket
CB8 7QA
Phone: 0638 750613
Fax:

Specialist in thongs of Sea Kale.

POYN

Poyntzfield Herb Nursery
Black Isle
By Dingwall
Ross-shire
Scotland
IV7 8LX
Phone: 03818 352
Fax:

Specialist herb nursery, with many unusual edible plants beyond those listed. Organically grown seeds and plants. Send 3x1st class stamps and SAE for catalogue.

RSLU

Royal Sluis Ltd
P.O. Box 34
Unit 24 Marathon Place
Moss Side Estate
Leyland
PR5 3QT
Phone:
Fax:

Bulk only.

ROB

W. Robinson & Sons Ltd
Sunny Bank
Forton
Nr Preston
Lancs
PR3 0BN
Phone: 0524 791210
Fax: 0524 791933

Specialist in giant and exhibition varieties.

ROG

R. V. Roger Ltd
The Nurseries
Pickering
North Yorkshire
YO18 7HG
Phone: 0751 72226
Fax:

Latest catalogue we have is from 1993.

F1 Many	F1 Unique	OP Many	OP Unique

Suppliers

SMM ▰▱▱▱▱

S.M.McArd (Seeds)
39 West Road
Pointon
Sleaford
Lincs
NG34 0NA
Phone:
Fax:

Bulk & small supplies. Good range of no-nonsense packets at keen prices.

SBS ▰▱▱▱▱

Seeds-By-Size
45 Crouchfield
Hemel Hempstead
Herts
HP1 1PA
Phone: 0442 251458
Fax:

An outstanding range of vegetable varieties.

SHAR ▰▱▱▱▱

Sharpes International Seeds Ltd
Sleaford
Lincs
NG34 7HA
Phone: 0529 304511
Fax: 0529 303908

Bulk, only. The company will accept orders for a minimum of 5 Kg, but all orders should be of multiples of 5 Kg.

SUFF ▰▱▱▱▱

Suffolk Herbs Ltd
Monks Farm
Coggeshall Road
Kelvedon
Essex
CO5 9PG
Phone: 0376 572456
Fax: 0376 571189

Recently taken over by E.W. King & Co. Has not affected their extensive list, which features many old European varieties.

SUTT ▰▱▱▱▱

Suttons Seeds Ltd
Hele Road
Torquay
Devon
TQ2 7QJ
Phone: 0803 614455
Fax: 0803 615747

T&M ▰▱▱▱▱

Thompson & Morgan (Ipswich) Ltd
Poplar Lane
Ipswich
Suffolk
IP8 3BU
Phone: 0473 688821
Fax: 0473 680199

Suppliers

TOZE
A.L. Tozer Ltd
Pyports
Downside Bridge Road
Cobham
SURREY
KT11 3EH
Phone: 0932 862059
Fax: 0932 868973
Larger quantities only.

TUCK
Edwin Tucker and Sons Ltd
Brewery Meadow
Stonepark, Ashburton
Newton Abbot
Devon
TQ13 7DG
Phone: 0364 652403
Fax: 0364 654300
Good potato list among many general seeds.

UNWI
Unwins Seeds Ltd
Mail Order Department
Histon
Cambridge
CB4 4ZZ
Phone: 0945 588522
Fax:

VANH
Van Hage Garden Company
Great Amwell
Ware
Herts
SG12 9RP
Phone: 0920 870811
Fax: 0920 871861
Specialises in Dutch varieties.

WKI
West Kington Nurseries Ltd
Pound Hill
West Kington
Near Chippenham
Wiltshire
SN14 7JG
Phone: 0249 782822
Fax: 0249 782953
New this year. Supplier of ornamentals, they also do thongs of true Sea Kale.

WALL
Wallis Seeds
Broads Green
Great Waltham
Chelmsford
Essex
CM3 1DS
Phone: 0245 360413
Fax:
General list, new to The Vegetable Finder this year.

F1 Many	F1 Unique	OP Many	OP Unique

Suppliers

WEBS ▨▨▨▨▨▨▨▨▨▨▨▨▨▨▨░░░

Websters Seed Potatoes
6 Denside
Letham Grange
Arbroath
Tayside
DD11 4QL
Phone: 024189 404
Fax:

Potato specialist. Despite problems with supply last season, Mr Webster insists that "we now intend concentrating solely on the Mail Order side of the business which will have my personal supervision".

YATE ████████▨▨▨▨▨▨▨▨▨░

Samuel Yates Ltd
Withyfold Drive
Macclesfield
Cheshire
SK10 2BE
Phone: 0625 427823
Fax: 0625 422843

Bulk only.

F1 Many	F1 Unique	OP Many	OP Unique